D0926018

QUANTUM ELECTRONICS

Quantum Electronics

BY

JOHN R. PIERCE

This book is the second volume of a revised and greatly
enlarged edition of *Electrons, Waves and Messages,* which
was published in 1956 by Doubleday & Company, Inc.

Published by Anchor Books
Doubleday & Company, Inc.
Garden City, New York

To Ellen

THE SCIENCE STUDY SERIES

The Science Study Series offers to students and to the general public the writing of distinguished authors on the most stirring and fundamental topics of science, from the smallest known particles to the whole universe. Some of the books tell of the role of science in the world of man, his technology and civilization. Others are biographical in nature, telling the fascinating stories of the great discoverers and their discoveries. All the authors have been selected both for expertness in the fields they discuss and for ability to communicate their special knowledge and their own views in an interesting way. The primary purpose of these books is to provide a survey within the grasp of the young student or the layman. Many of the books, it is hoped, will encourage the reader to make his own investigations of natural phenomena.

The Series, which now offers topics in all the sciences and their applications, had its beginning in a project to revise the secondary schools' physics curriculum. At the Massachusetts Institute of Technology during 1956 a group of physicists, high school teachers, journalists, apparatus designers, film producers, and other specialists organized the Physical Science Study Committee, now operating as a part of Educational Services Incorporated, Watertown, Massachusetts. They pooled their knowledge and experience toward the design and creation of aids to the learning of physics. Initially their effort was supported by the National Science Foundation, which has continued to aid the program. The Ford Foundation, the Fund for the Advancement of Education, and the Alfred P. Sloan Foundation have also given support. The Committee has created a text book, an extensive film series, a laboratory guide, especially designed apparatus, and a teacher's source book.

The Series is guided by a Board of Editors consisting of Bruce F. Kingsbury, Managing Editor; John H. Durston, General Editor; Paul F. Brandwein, the Conservation Foundation and Harcourt, Brace & World, Inc.; Samuel A. Goudsmit, Brookhaven National Laboratory; Philippe LeCorbeiller, Harvard University; and Gerard Piel, *Scientific American*.

BIOGRAPHICAL FOREWORD

Quantum Electronics is a sequel to John R. Pierce's *Electrons and Waves,* which was published in the Science Study Series in 1964. The two together (along with a third volume to come) constitute a general updating, a thorough revision, and a major extension of his *Electrons, Waves and Messages* (Doubleday & Company, 1956). Most of the material in *Quantum Electronics* is new.

In the last thirty years some scientists have managed to make a public bugbear out of quantum theory. It is too mathematical, they have told us time and again, it is too radically removed from accustomed ways of thinking, for any layman to understand. The extreme position (and the fashionable one!) has been to dismiss all efforts at verbal explanation and to insist that modern theoretical physics has no meaning, or even reality, outside the very complex and abstract mathematics in which it is expressed.

Dr. Pierce, however, is of the growing school that believes that not all the ideas of quantum theory, and certainly not its goals, are beyond the layman's appreciation. Happily, this school now can draw support from some of the highly technical devices that in very recent years have been developed on the foundations of quantum theory. These devices, which you will find discussed in detail in *Quantum Electronics,* do in fact operate on quantum laws, and their operations can be described in words that every intelligent reader can follow. One might say that these devices provide Dr. Pierce and other sympathetic writers on science for laymen with a demonstration apparatus with which to illustrate their lectures.

Still, it would not be playing fair to suggest that the lay reader can master quantum theory in one easy lesson. To get even an idea of what modern physics is about calls for concentration and reading. It is not amiss here to suggest some books for collateral reading that will enrich the reader's grasp of Dr. Pierce's books and that in turn will be enriched by Dr. Pierce's own insights and his method of presentation.

First on the list, of course, is *Electrons and Waves.* Every author of a sequel has the right to assume familiarity with the preceding volume, and Dr. Pierce, with propriety, takes it for granted in *Quantum Electronics* that his readers will have been through *Electrons and Waves.* His careful laying of the groundwork (or its equivalent by another equally sympathetic author) is indispensable to full understanding of the subject matter of this book.

Two other books in the Science Study Series cover almost the same topics of quantum theory but from quite different points of view. George Gamow in *The Thirty Years That Shook Physics* traces the historical development of quantum theory and enlivens his account with personal anecdotes about his own part in it and about the famous physicists he knew. Alec T. Stewart in *Perpetual Motion* approaches quantum theory by way of solid state physics, the behavior of atoms in crystals. A third book in the Series that is pertinent but not directly concerned with quantum theory is _Sound Waves and Light Waves_ by Winston E. Kock. Using the latest designs of antennas and wave lenses as examples, he brings to bear on the electromagnetic field much the same scheme of expository attack that Dr. Pierce has directed so successfully against quantum theory.

Dr. Pierce through most of his productive career has been associated with the Bell Laboratories and is one of America's outstanding electronic engineers. He was born on March 27, 1910, at Des Moines, Iowa. From boyhood interested in mathematics, electric circuitry and vacuum tubes, he received his B.S. in 1933 from the California Institute of Technology. The M.S. followed in the next year and the Ph.D. in 1936, also from Caltech. He joined Bell Labs after receiving the doctorate.

Dr. Pierce's professional career has taken him into many fields of investigation, radio, electronics, acoustics and vision, mathematics, computation, and psychology. He has been Executive Director, Research-Communications Principles and Systems Divisions, at Bell. An analysis he made in 1954 led directly (if not smoothly) to the 1960 launching of Project Echo, the forerunner of TELSTAR, the opening signal for the age of international communication by satellite. He received the 1963 National Medal of Science.

Dr. Pierce credits the science fiction of Jules Verne, H. G. Wells, and Hugo Gernsback with having excited his interest in science, and he himself has composed in the genre, under the nom de plume "J. J. Coupling." His serious writing includes, besides _Electrons, Waves and Messages, Theory and_

Design of Electric Beams (Van Nostrand, 1949); *Traveling Wave Tubes* (Van Nostrand, 1950); *Man's World of Sound,* in collaboration with Edward E. David, Jr. (Doubleday, 1958); *Waves and the Ear,* in collaboration with Willem A. van Bergeijk and Edward E. David, Jr. (Science Study Series, 1960); *Symbols, Signals and Noise* (Harper & Row, 1961), and many articles in general magazines and technical journals.

He has received the following awards: Eta Kappa Nu, 1942; Morris Liebmann Memorial Prize, 1947; Stuart Ballantine Medal, 1960; Air Force Association H. H. Arnold Trophy, 1962; the Golden Plate Award of the Academy of Achievement, 1962; the Arnold Air Society General Hoyt S. Vandenberg Trophy, 1963; and the following honorary degrees: D.Eng. from the Newark College of Engineering, 1961; D.Sc. from Northwestern University, 1961; D.Sc. from Yale University, 1963; D.Sc. from Polytechnic Institute of Brooklyn, 1963.

Dr. Pierce is a member of the National Academy of Sciences and the Air Force Association, and a Fellow of the American Academy of Arts and Sciences, the Institute of Electrical and Electronics Engineers, the American Physical Society, the Acoustical Society of America, the American Astronautical Society, and the British Interplanetary Society. He is a Kentucky colonel.

John H. Durston

PREFACE

When I set out to revise and extend *Electrons, Waves and Messages* (Doubleday & Company, 1956) for publication in the Science Study Series,* I found it necessary to include a good deal of new material in order to explain masers, lasers, and transistors. On going over the first revision John H. Durston, of Educational Services Incorporated, pointed out that the new material could best be expanded to form this separate volume. His particular suggestions toward this end were helpful. I have tried to meet one of them by including an appendix on mathematical notation which may help some readers to understand the few equations in the text.

Also, I owe a good deal of particular advice, criticism, and help to J. P. Gordon, who read the first four chapters in two different versions.

I wish to acknowledge my debt to the Desert Research Institute of the University of Nevada, where I first drafted these chapters. Finally, I owe a debt to Miss Florence M. Costello and Miss Elizabeth La Jeunesse, who saw that the book was finally typed, the figures prepared, and other wearing details taken care of.

J. R. Pierce

* The first volume of the revision, *Electrons and Waves,* was published by Anchor Books, Doubleday & Company, Inc., Garden City, New York, as a part of the Science Study Series, in 1964. This first volume is referred to in the text of this book as *Electrons and Waves.*

CONTENTS

QUANTUM ELECTRONICS

Chapter I

KNOWING THE WORLD

We all sometimes wonder about things remote from our immediate surroundings or beyond the reach of our senses. We would like to know what happens in far lands, what happened in the past, or what will happen in the future. The money spent on travel, television, newspapers, magazines and books, including historical novels and science fiction, is a measure of this human curiosity. But sometimes we want to know more deeply about things that we encounter in everyday life—and our curiosity takes in telephones and television and transistor radios.

Ten years ago we had telephones and television, but we did not have transistor radios. Today the multitudes of teen-agers who play them full blast in the bus, on the beach or at the ball game are acutely aware of transistor radios, and any adults within earshot are even more so.

Not many who have heard a transistor radio have seen a transistor, and only a few of those who have seen one understand how it operates. I propose that through reading this book you can find out how a transistor operates, and much else besides. But to understand the transistor and other related devices you will have to learn something new and different from what you would have needed to know a decade ago in order to understand a telephone or a television set or a radio of that day. In the last ten years something quite revolutionary has taken place in electronics. This development is the invention and use of devices whose very existence and operation depend on the laws of quantum physics. These devices include the transistor and the maser and the laser.

Physical theory forms a basis for explaining and exploiting natural phenomena. Newton's laws of motion and of gravitation tell us how planets move about the sun and make it possible to predict and control the orbits of missiles and satellites. Maxwell's equations explain the propagation of light and make it possible to design radio antennas and microwave communication systems. The laws of quantum physics, or *quantum mechanics,* explain a wide variety of physical and chemical phenomena.

A Science of Precision Laws

We now know that Newton's laws of motion and Maxwell's equations are only approximate laws of nature, which work well for large bodies and for changes that are not too rapid. The laws of quantum mechanics are better laws, for they enable us to understand and, in masers and lasers and transistors, to make use of physical phenomena involving bodies as small as atoms and ions, and changes as rapid as the vibrations of light.

In the realm of the large and the slow, quantum mechanics is consistent with what we observe about us in everyday life—skating, throwing a ball, whirling a weight on a string, or dropping a stone in a pool of water. But we can understand such behavior of matter through understanding Newton's laws, which are accurate for objects large enough to be visible and motions slow enough to be appreciated by the eye. The characteristic and new features of quantum mechanics are directly apparent only in laboratory experiments. Yet the laws of quantum mechanics explaining such experiments give an adequate and valid picture of the operation of such important devices as transistors, masers, and lasers, and an insight into many otherwise puzzling problems as well.

Almost everyone has heard of quantum mechanics, and questions are raised invariably when quantum mechanics is mentioned. Is quantum mechanics terribly difficult compared with Newtonian or classical mechanics or with Maxwell's equations? Here I should like to paraphrase remarks by two of my friends. One said that it doesn't take much quantum mechanics to get quantitative answers to many problems concerning masers and lasers. The other said that the quantum-mechanical treatment of even a very simple problem (for example, the propagation of a sinusoidal electromagnetic wave along a lossy transmission line) can be terribly difficult. Both observations are true.

I don't know how to write down any version of quantum mechanics that is as simple, comprehensive, and tractable as Newton's laws of motion or Maxwell's equations. Perhaps the trouble lies in my ignorance. Or it may lie in the state of development and formulation of quantum mechanics. Or quantum mechanics may be inherently difficult in the sense that it calls for mathematical skill that is neither generally available nor easily supplied.

There is another frequently asked question about quantum mechanics. Is quantum mechanics reasonable? Or does it somehow fly in the face of experience and common sense?

If the reader hasn't objected already to this second question, I propose to. I think that the question is both natural and confused. Certainly quantum mechanics does not fly in the face of experience; it is in accord with experience. But some quantum-mechanical phenomena are at odds with conclusions people often jump to on the basis of their experience outside of the laboratory.

This matter of the relation of common experience to the world of the molecule and the atom merits a general discussion. I think we must all have wondered how the world about us would appear to a giant or to a Lilliputian. When the microscope extended man's powers of observation it excited his curiosity. Fitz-James O'Brien, an imaginative nineteenth-century writer, was inspired by the wonders of the microscope to speculate on what an observer might see with an instrument much more powerful than any that had been built. In a story called *The Diamond Lens,* he told of a microscopist who saw a minute but lovely girl in a molecule of water.

Can we pursue such a road to a deeper examination and understanding of nature? Only in the imagination, and then only in the imagination of those who are ignorant of the laws of nature. For we know that we can see only those details of the structure of matter that are large compared with a wavelength of light. Further, as the aperture of a lens (either the lens of a microscope or the lens of an eye) becomes smaller in comparison with the wavelength of light the detail in the images it forms decreases. If a Lilliputian and his books were both made smaller and smaller eventually he would be unable to read the books. But he could not comprehend the text even if he could see it; there would not be room in his skull for enough brain cells to duplicate our complicated (and thereby literate) nervous organization.

In our full-size world we have eyes, ears, fingers, and tongues, and we can use voltmeters and ammeters to measure voltages and currents, electroscopes to measure charge, magnetometers to measure magnetic fields, and spring balances to measure forces. But we cannot shrink either ourselves, our senses, or our measuring instruments to explore the ultimate constitution of matter, the nature of electrons, or the behavior of electric and magnetic fields on a very minute scale.

A child might ask, is an electron shiny or dull? A shiny object is shiny because it has surface irregularities small compared with a wavelength of light, while a dull object is dull because it has surface irregularities large compared with a wavelength of light, and so scatters light. I suppose we could say that an electron is shiny, but not in any sense that would have meaning for a child. What does an electron taste like? With what mouth shall we taste it? Is it hard or soft? With what finger shall we touch it? Yet a determined child might insistently demand answers to questions of this sort.

In the world of our immediate senses we encounter phenomena which we wish to organize, to predict, to use. These phenomena include meter readings, flashes of light emitted when electrons strike a thin layer of a fluorescent substance covering a glass surface (that is, when electrons strike a *fluorescent screen*), and the amplification of weak signals to produce audible sounds. The business of science is to enable us to "understand" these and other phenomena by means of quantitative relations among them and predictions concerning them. Science need not answer such seemingly plausible questions as what is the taste or the color of an electron.

In the gross world about us we can observe *particles,* or little bits of matter. We can also observe waves. Waves may be a vibration of matter, as are sound waves and waves on water. Waves can also be varying electric and magnetic fields which move from place to place; the electromagnetic waves of radio and television consist of such fluctuating, traveling electric and magnetic fields.

Through observation of nature we can become as familiar with waves and particles and their behavior as we are with touch, taste, and color. Thus, we are likely to ask, is an electron a particle or is it a wave? Or does light consist of particles (photons), or does it consist of waves? Need we or can we really answer such questions? How do they square with reality?

Light: Particles or Waves

Figure 1 illustrates one sort of experiment which might help us to answer such questions.[1] To the left is a distant source of light of a single frequency and wavelength, whose rays strike a plate with two very narrow parallel slits cut through it. The slits must be narrow compared with a wavelength of light. The light passing through the slits falls on a very thin layer of material called a *photoemitter,* which gives off electrons on the far side when light strikes it. These electrons, accelerated and focused, strike a

[1] It would be possible to carry out this experiment as illustrated, but actually the results are inferred from the outcome of a number of simpler experiments not as easy to describe. Further, the two slits of Fig. 1 would have to be very narrow (around 10^{-5} centimeters wide) and very close together.

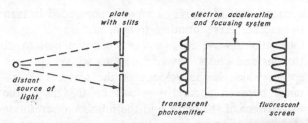

FIGURE 1

flat fluorescent screen at a high velocity. When an electron strikes, the screen emits a flash of light. Thus, the pattern of electron emission which the light on the transparent photoemitter causes is reproduced on the fluorescent screen as a pattern of light or flashes of light. If light is "really" waves, we should expect to see on the screen a pattern consisting of bright and dark bands parallel to the slit. This is a phenomenon called *wave interference* or *diffraction* and it is characteristic of all waves.

When a wave travels past an observer, some quantity rises and falls regularly in amplitude. This periodicity is illustrated symbolically in Fig. 2. In a wave on water we have a maximum or *crest,* suc-

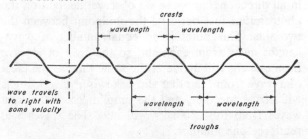

FIGURE 2

ceeded by a minimum or *trough,* succeeded in turn by another crest, another trough, and so on. If we look at the wave as a whole we see a pattern of troughs and crests traveling past us with a constant speed, which is the velocity of the wave. The distance between successive crests or troughs is the *wavelength* of the wave and the number of crests or troughs passing us in a second is the *frequency* of the wave. Successive maxima and minima of a wave may be crests and troughs, as in a wave on water; or successive increases and decreases in pressure, as in a sound wave; or electric or magnetic fields successively in opposite directions, as in an electromagnetic wave.

Whatever sort of waves we have, if two waves of equal strength overlap so that crests (or their equivalent) coincide with crests, and troughs (or their equivalent) with troughs, the over-all wave, that is, the sum of the two waves, will be stronger than either one alone. If, however, the crest of one wave falls on the trough of a wave of equal strength, the two waves will cancel, and the two waves together give nothing.

If light is a wave, then when light passes through the two slits, which are narrow compared with a wavelength, waves of light will travel from each slit in all directions. Suppose we observe the light on the photoemitter just opposite the midpoint between the two slits. This point is an equal number of wavelengths away from each slit, so the crest of a wave from one slit will arrive at the same time as the crest of a wave from the other slit. Likewise, wave troughs will arrive together, and the amplitudes of the light waves from the two slits will add. The waves will reinforce one another.

As we move upward along the photoemitter, we will move closer to the upper slit and farther away from the lower slit. Soon we will reach a point at which the crest of the wave from one slit will arrive when the trough of the wave from the other slit arrives. At this point, the waves of light from the two slits will cancel; there will be no light, and no electron will leave the photoemitter. The wiggly curve drawn at the photoemitter illustrates the brightness or power of the light as a function of distance up or down from the midpoint between the slits. Because the rate of emission of electrons increases with the intensity of the light, this curve also gives the rate at which electrons leave the photoemitter surface. The pattern of light is thus reproduced on the fluorescent screen to the right, where the accelerated and focused electrons strike it. When such an experiment is carried out, all is in accord with the behavior of waves. If we cover up one of the slits, there will be no wiggly interference pattern; instead, there will be a uniform illumination of the photoemitter and a uniform flow of electrons, giving a uniform illumination on the fluorescent screen. It seems that light must be waves!

Photons: Packets of Energy

But let us now consider a different phenomenon. It takes a considerable energy to liberate an electron from the photoemitter. We might think that if we cut down the intensity of the light it would no longer have enough energy to liberate an electron. But the rate at which electrons are liberated is strictly proportional to the energy flow, that is, to the power of the light. It is as if this energy were concentrated into little pellets, each capable of causing the emission of an electron. A weak light, then, would mean fewer pellets, not a less energetic effect. This phenomenon seems to argue that light comes in little pellets or particles, which we can call photons.

Physicists came reluctantly to the idea of pellets or photons of light, because for years the diffraction of light had shown so clearly that the behavior of light is like that of a wave. Max Planck took the first step. He showed in 1900 that the experimentally observed intensity of the electromagnetic radiation in an enclosure or "black box" held at a given temperature could be explained only if it was assumed that radiation of a particular frequency could have only certain particular amounts of energy. These particular amounts of energy are all multiples of hf, where f is the frequency of the radiation, and $h = 6.62 \times 10^{-34}$ joule seconds[2] is Planck's constant. This description is consistent with the idea that light is made up of little packets of energy, or photons, each with an energy of hf joules, but it does not prove the existence of photons; it only makes them plausible.

In 1905, Albert Einstein wrote a paper on the photoelectric effect for which he received the Nobel Prize. At that time experiments had shown that the energy with which individual electrons leave a photoemitter does not increase as the intensity or power of the beam of light causing the emission of the electrons increases. One simply gets more electrons with a more powerful light, not speedier electrons. Einstein explained this situation by assuming that the

[2] A joule is an amount of energy. A power of one watt means an expenditure of one joule of energy per second. Hence, to light a 100-watt light bulb requires the expenditure of 100 joules of energy per second.

energy of the light beam is bunched into packets of energy, each with an energy hf. (It was Einstein who gave the name *photon* to these packets of energy.) He pointed out that any photon falling on a photo-emitter can cause the emission of an electron, so the rate at which electrons are emitted is proportional to the rate at which photons reach the surface, and hence to the joules per second, or power, of the light. The most energy an electron leaving the surface can have, however, is the energy of the single photon that caused its emission.

Further, for a particular photoemitter it takes some particular least energy to cause the emission of an electron. If we keep the power of the light constant but decrease the frequency f, for a given photoemit-ter there is some critical frequency below which no electron will be emitted, even with a rather high intensity of light. A photon of light below this fre-quency simply has not enough energy to liberate an electron from that particular photoemitter.

Physicists have found these and other arguments overwhelming, and no one now doubts that light (and the rest of electromagnetic radiation as well, including radio waves) comes in discrete amounts of energy, or photons. One easily comes to think of the photons of light as consisting of little particles, each with an energy hf, rather than as waves.

The Uncertainty Principle

But, we ask, when the light is weak and we see only occasional flashes on the fluorescent screen, cor-responding to the arrival of occasional individual photons at the photoemitter, which slit does a particular photon go through? We can make sure of this by covering one of the slits—but then the wiggly interference pattern, with more light striking the photoemitter surface and more electrons emitted at some points than at others, disappears. When one slit is covered, the electrons are just as likely to come from one part of the photoemitter as from another.

The existence of an interference pattern does not depend on the intensity of the light. We can have an interference pattern (that is, photons can strike some portions of the photoemitter more frequently than others) even when photons arrive seconds apart, but we obtain an interference pattern only if both slits are open. So there is an uncertainty as to the direction from which the photon reaches the photoemitter—that is, an uncertainty as to what its momentum[3] is.

Here we touch upon a general principle of quantum mechanics which has several important consequences in quantum electronics. This is the *uncertainty principle,* which Werner Heisenberg enunciated in 1927. We will consider the uncertainty principle only as illustrated in one particular sort of measurement, though the principle applies to measurements of other quantities as well.

Heisenberg's uncertainty principle relates the least uncertainty one can have as to position of arrival of a photon and the uncertainty as to the momentum of the photon. In a given apparatus one uncertainty can be small only if the other is large. An example is the relation between the sharpness of an image and the diameter of the lens which produces it. The

[3] Momentum is a fundamental quantity in physics, defined as mass multiplied by velocity. See pages 42–46, *Electrons and Waves.*

larger the lens (if it is free of aberration), the sharper the image. But the larger the diameter of the lens, the wider is the range of directions from which a photon can approach a given part of the image. Momentum is a vector quantity with direction as well as magnitude, and hence an uncertainty in direction means an uncertainty in momentum.

In a mathematical formulation of Heisenberg's uncertainty principle, physicists make use of the fact that in quantum mechanics what we know concerning position can be described by one wave pattern or "wave function,"[4] and what we know concerning momentum by another wave function. The momentum wave function is the *Fourier transform*[5] of the position wave function.

The relation between a function and its Fourier transform is like that between an electric pulse and the bandwidth of frequencies which make up or represent the pulse; this is discussed briefly in Chapter Eight of *Electrons and Waves*. Here I will say only that the Fourier transform of a narrow, precise, wave function is a very broad wave function, while

[4] A wave function is a mathematical description of a wave, which tells how the intensity of the wave varies from point to point in space. In the quantum-mechanical theory of light, the position wave function tells us the probability of observing a photon in any designated place, and the momentum wave function tells us the probability of observing a photon with any designated momentum.

[5] A French mathematician, Baron Jean Baptiste Joseph Fourier (1768–1830) showed that a curve can be represented by a sum of sine waves of different wavelengths. For instance, the vibration of a stretched string of length L can be represented as a sum of sine waves of wavelengths L, L/2, L/3, etc. A Fourier transform of a function (a wave function, for example) represents the function as sine waves of a continuous range of wavelengths, from infinity to zero.

a very broad wave function can have a very narrow, precise Fourier transform.

The general problem of measurement of such quantities as position and momentum in quantum mechanics is a recondite one, and in this book I will try to stick to very simple examples which do not appear to raise embarrassing questions.

In the apparatus of Fig. 1, if the photons reach a photoemitter from one very narrow slit, what one knows is the position of the photon as it passes through the slit; hence, its momentum must be uncertain, and we cannot know its direction of motion. Thus, when photons go through a single very narrow slit, we cannot predict where they will fall on the photoemitter.

Suppose, however, that a photon may have come through one slit or the other. We are uncertain concerning its position at the time when it passes the slits, but by this very uncertainty of its position we are able to make some prediction concerning momentum or direction of motion and hence concerning where the photon can hit the screen. The photon will be likely to fall in certain bands or strips parallel to the slits and unlikely to fall in other bands or strips. We make this prediction by treating light as a wave, as we have outlined.

Light, it becomes evident, has properties that we usually associate with waves, and it has properties that we usually associate with particles.

The Behavior of Electrons

What about electrons, which we ordinarily think of as particles? Fig. 3 shows an experiment with electrons analogous to the experiment with light il-

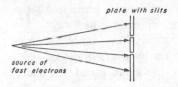

FIGURE 3

lustrated in Fig. 1.[6] To the left we have a distant
source of very energetic electrons, all with the same
speed. The source might be some radioactive material or else a hot filament and an accelerating voltage.
To the right we have a plate with slits. Farther on
we have a fluorescent screen. Again we see on the
fluorescent screen a wiggly diffraction pattern, as in
the case of light. Are electrons waves? If the electrons arrive infrequently, we see individual bright
flashes on the fluorescent screen, as if little particles
are striking the screen. Which slit did a particular
particle go through? If we close up one slit to make
sure, the wiggly diffraction pattern disappears and
electrons are equally likely to strike any portion of
the screen. We are in a dilemma if we insist that
electrons must behave either like stones (standing for
particles) or like ripples on a pond (standing for
waves).

What we experience directly in the physical world
about us are phenomena that involve many photons
or many electrons, and these phenomena are different from each other because photons and electrons,

[6] It would be very difficult, if not impossible, to carry out
the experiment as illustrated, particularly because the slits
would have to be so narrow and accurate. The results are
inferred from other experiments less easy to describe. The
slits of Fig. 3 would have to be even closer together than in
the light experiment of Fig. 1.

while they share the wavelike and particlelike behavior we have described, differ in other ways.

Both photons and electrons have mass and momentum; both are acted on by a gravitational field. But photons always have the same speed, the speed of light; they can differ in momentum only by traveling in different directions and they can differ in energy only by having different frequencies. Electrons can have any velocity less than the speed of light. They are acted on by electric and magnetic fields, which do not directly affect photons. And the wavelengths of electrons traveling with any speed we ordinarily encounter are much shorter than the wavelength of visible light.

There is another distinction, as well, which is vitally important. This has to do with the behavior of many photons or of many electrons.

Any number of photons can act in concert, all forming part of the same electromagnetic wave pattern or wave function. A flow of coordinated or coherent photons can be a sharply focused beam of light or radio waves. Or, if the photons are trapped in a highly reflecting closed box or *resonator,* the photons can form a *standing wave,* similar to the vibration of a plucked string. When we measure the electric and magnetic field strengths of a strong coherent electromagnetic field at various points in a beam or in a box, we are dealing with a multitude of photons, and we get a sort of smooth average behavior. The uncertainty principle tells us that we cannot measure simultaneously both the electric and magnetic fields with perfect accuracy, but the effect is so small that we see it only in very special circumstances. The uncertainty shows up as a fluctuation or noise when we try to measure very weak waves very accurately.

Photons can be trapped in a reflecting box. Electrons can be trapped in a magnetic field or by the positive nucleus of an atom. But only one electron can have a particular wave pattern. There is no electron analogue of a coherent electromagnetic wave consisting of many photons with the same wave pattern. A beam of electrons *must* be different from a coherent beam of light. In a gross way, a beam of light is strongly like a wave, while a beam of electrons is strongly like a jet of individual particles.

When we find order in a system of electrons we find something very different from a coherent beam of light. Orderly systems of many electrons and atomic nuclei are solid crystalline substances. Atoms of matter consist of nuclei surrounded by electrons, and crystals of matter consist of arrays of nuclei, each holding some electrons fast and sharing others. Different electrons form different wave patterns or wave functions, but the different patterns are related through the periodic regularity of the crystal.

In our gross world we can make of such crystals small particles or pellets which in their gross motions show no detectable wavelike properties. But experiments show very clearly the wavelike behavior of the electrons in the crystals. Perhaps very precise experiments could show the wavelike properties of small enough particles of various materials and compounds. Certainly, even very strong light waves, which to most tests seem smooth and wavelike, release electrons one by one from a photoemitter in a way that suggests bombardment by particles. Have we in both electrons and light an irresolvable conflict between particle and wave?

New Concepts for the Submicroscopic Realm

As I see it, the seemingly pure wavelike and pure particlelike behaviors we encounter in the gross world about us are abstractions or approximations; for those things that we can observe directly or with gross instruments the approximations are so nearly valid as to seem perfect and inescapable. But in the submicroscopic realm of electrons and photons we can never find an experiment that will distinguish between "ideal particle" and "ideal wave." To ask whether an electron or a photon is a particle or a wave is to ask an unanswerable and unsophisticated question. It is like asking about the color or the taste of an electron.

We can characterize chunks of matter as particles, and beams of light as waves. We can perform many experiments that distinguish clearly between the behavior of such particles and waves. Yet particles and waves are simplified abstractions which at best describe nature approximately, though often so exceedingly well that there is no detectable error.

If we make fine enough measurements we see that nature really does not have in it that sharp distinction of kind that we have put into our simplified and useful concepts of particle and wave. It is the very phenomena for which the dichotomy of particle and wave is meaningless that are vitally important in quantum electronics.

Applications of Quantum Phenomena

If this were a book about quantum mechanics in general, I could proceed with a host of other interesting illustrative examples of quantum phenomena. But this book is about quantum electronics. What I have tried to do in this chapter is to provide a background that will help to make the structure and behavior of electronic devices, including the maser, the laser and the transistor, more palatable to the person who understands something of Newton's laws of motion and the laws of electricity and magnetism, but who knows less about quantum phenomena. Thus quantum phenomena will not be the subject of further exposition, but a means for understanding various devices and problems.

We will see how Heisenberg's uncertainty principle leads inevitably to fuzziness or *noise* in the amplification of very weak radio or light signals. We will see how the emission of a photon of discrete energy by an excited atom, molecule or ion is the essential basis of the operation of the maser and the laser. We will see how the wavelike behavior of electrons is essential to the picture we have of the motions of electrons through the semiconducting material of a transistor. Our further concern will be the practical consequences and applications of quantum phenomena in such devices and processes.

Yet, as I said at the beginning of this chapter, we all wonder; we want to understand. I myself ask, do I really understand what I have heard about quantum phenomena, and does what I have heard satisfy me? Surely, there is much about quantum phenomena that I don't understand, or am not even familiar with. And from time to time I keep asking myself questions (which slit *did* the photon or electron go through?) that appear to be unanswerable because there is no measurement that can tell. The reader is welcome to share a feeling of unease and confusion that many others as well as I have had about quantum mechanics. But I *know* that quantum mechanics has led to the understanding of and (in the case of the maser and the laser) to the invention of devices of great practical importance, and this accomplishment seems more important to me than any feelings which from time to time may perturb me.

Chapter II

NOISE

Across the noisy room one can scarcely distinguish a single voice; the words are lost in the confused babble of sound waves; they are drowned out by noise. The same voice can be heard clearly when at last the guests leave. On a still night in the open, over water perhaps, the voice will carry much farther. Beyond a certain distance, however, the sound will be so weak that we cannot understand it.

Will it help to pick the sound up with a microphone, to amplify it with a transistor, and to listen to the amplified sound with a telephone receiver? It will help a little, perhaps, but with the amplifier we will hear the weak noises of the still night made large also. Limitless amplification of sounds is no more effective than limitless magnification of tiny objects. Beyond a certain distance words cannot be distinguished, no matter how powerful an amplifier we may use. Noise drowns out the voice.

The case of radio signals is exactly analogous. In listening to stations in the broadcast band during the summer we are often annoyed by the crackle and fry of the static associated with thunderstorms. More distant stations may be drowned out in a steady hiss of noise, even in clear winter weather. The pictures from distant TV stations are obscured by an appearance of "snow," a fine-grained, fluctuating pattern which is the counterpart of the hiss of noise in the radio receiver. This pattern, too, and the electrical signal producing it, are called *noise* by engineers and physicists. To an electronics engineer, the currents and voltages in the circuit of a radio receiver, a TV set, or any other electrical circuit constitute either a signal—that is, something put there purposefully—or noise, something that gets there in spite of the engineer's efforts to exclude it. Noise is something that tends to obscure the signal and render it unintelligible.

Radio receivers receive noise as well as signals. Radio receivers also produce noise themselves. We can use low-power transmitters to send radio signals short distances. Because of noise, we must use transmitters of higher power to send signals longer distances. Increasing the amplification of the receiver is not enough to enable us to hear a weak transmitter if it is very far away. As we increase the amplification beyond a certain point, we will merely hear, or see, an intense noise.

Is noise really a fundamental limitation on radio communication? As some locations and some times are quieter in the everyday sense, as a still night is quieter than a noisy room, so, too, some times and some places are quieter than others in an electrical sense. Short-wave radio transmission, which provides transoceanic telephony to many far lands, is generally quieter in the tropical regions than it is near the North Pole. Calls in northern latitudes are better in winter than in summer, and they are better in periods of low sunspot activity than in periods of high sunspot activity. Radio communication may be very noisy if not altogether impossible during the magnetic storms caused when bursts of charged particles reach us from the sun. These defects in quality, as well as the limitation on the number of short-wave channels, favor overseas communication by submarine cable or by communication satellites rather than by short-wave radio.

In the early, long-wave days of radio various forms of strong static picked up by the antenna dominated and obscured other forms of noise. As higher and higher frequencies were exploited it was found that, as the frequency is increased, noise becomes less variable and less intense. In the broadcast band (around 1 megacycle) we are much troubled by summer thunderstorms. FM and TV (around 100 megacycles) are less troubled by such static, but we are likely to hear or see on FM or TV the noise generated by the ignition systems of passing cars, the noise from the sparks of the spark plugs. The sorts of noise that are generated by thunderstorms and accidently by man-made devices tend to disappear at high enough frequencies.

Johnson, or Thermal, Noise

Not all noise disappears at high frequencies. By 1928, working at a frequency of 20 megacycles, Harald T. Friis had constructed a radio receiver so sensitive that a fundamental, unavoidable noise in its input called Johnson noise or thermal noise could be detected. It was, in fact, this unprecedentedly sensitive radio receiver that enabled Karl Jansky to discover cosmic radio noise, and so to take the first crucial step into the revolutionary new field of radio astronomy.

At still higher frequencies, in the microwave range (thousands of megacycles), neither storms nor electrical machinery produce appreciable noise. The noise reaching the receiver antenna has fallen to the level of Johnson noise, a noise associated with all the objects in the universe. Johnson noise is the low-frequency portion of the electromagnetic radiation sent out by all hot bodies and, indeed, by any bodies with temperature above absolute zero. It was the spectrum of electromagnetic radiation associated with hot bodies that Max Planck explained satisfactorily, in 1900, in the first step toward our understanding of quantum phenomena. Thus, the very phenomenon that constitutes a fundamental limitation in electrical communication is also a fundamental quantum phenomenon.

Heat is a form of motion, a tiny, chaotic motion, and the temperature of an object tells us how intense the agitation of its molecules is. When water reaches the boiling point the motion of its molecules becomes so intense that the molecules no longer stick together as a liquid. When water is cooled the motion becomes less intense, and finally, at the freezing point, the motion of the molecules becomes small enough so that the forces between the molecules can consolidate the substance into the solid we call ice. The molecules of ice still move, but they move by vibrating, by oscillating about their mean positions. In fact, we can regard the vibration that constitutes heat in solids, such as ice, as chaotic sound waves traveling in all directions, much like the sound in a noisy room, but less intense and of an amplitude determined entirely by the temperature of the solid substance.

We can, indeed, sometimes observe a motion of tiny particles, a motion which constitutes heat. When the Scottish botanist Robert Brown (1773–

1858) looked at tiny particles of pollen under a microscope he saw them jumping about. The agitated molecules hit the tiny visible particles and cause the particles to move erratically. Motions due to thermal vibration can also be observed in the random rotation of objects suspended from very fine fibers of quartz. For instance, the mirrors of sensitive galvanometers swing erratically with thermal motions.

The molecules of substances are made up of atoms. All atoms contain electrons and protons, which are charged particles. As the atoms of a substance vibrate with the motion that is heat they send out chaotic electromagnetic waves of many frequencies. In quantum-mechanical terms they emit photons of many different energies. These waves or photons give rise to the ultimate, unavoidable electrical noise from which we suffer in the electronic art, even at microwave frequencies.

The Calculation of Electromagnetic Energy

The emission of electromagnetic radiation or photons by hot substances, besides being a plague to microwave communication, is the process by which energy gets to us from the sun. Such thermal radiation of electromagnetic waves deserves the careful attention of anyone interested in either physics or engineering. The first step in the investigation is to calculate the intensity of the chaotic thermal electromagnetic radiation due to heat and determine how its energy varies with temperature. Physicists attack the problem by considering electromagnetic radiation in a closed box with reflecting walls. Such a box acts as an electromagnetic resonator with many different modes or patterns of oscillation, just as a violin string or an organ pipe has many resonant frequencies at which it can vibrate. Each mode or spatial pattern has a particular frequency of oscillation. The spatial patterns of the electric and magnetic fields of these different modes or patterns of oscillation are different, and these spatial patterns are very complicated.

The way the electric and magnetic fields vary from point to point in the closed box depends on the sums of the fields of all the modes or patterns. The fields of each mode or pattern oscillate extremely rapidly with time and with the resonant frequency of the mode; the amplitude of each mode of oscillation varies more slowly with time. Hence, the over-all field, the sum of all the complicated field patterns of the various modes, fluctuates in an almost inconceivably complicated way.

However, the average energy in a particular mode of oscillation depends solely on the temperature. It is possible to calculate the number of different modes of oscillation lying in a given range of frequencies. If, for a given temperature, we can calculate the average electromagnetic energy in each mode of oscillation, we can then calculate the electromagnetic energy in a particular range of frequencies, and we can also calculate the total electromagnetic energy in the box.

In 1900, Lord Rayleigh and James (later Sir James) Jeans made such calculations. The energy they calculated agreed with the experimentally observed energy for low frequencies. Their calculations did not agree with experiment for high-frequency light (violet and ultraviolet). Moreover, their calculations said that the total electromagnetic energy in the box should be infinite!

Let us see how Rayleigh and Jeans went wrong and what Planck did that gave the correct result.

Planck's Constant

There is some curve that gives the fraction of the time that the energy in a mode of oscillation of the box will lie in some small fixed range. Rayleigh and Jeans had every reason to believe that this should be the Boltzmann distribution curve, which Ludwig Boltzmann derived toward the end of the last century to describe the distribution of kinetic energy among the molecules of a gas. The Boltzmann distribution curve is shown in Fig. 4; the horizontal scale is the

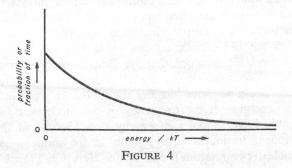

FIGURE 4

energy in the mode, E, divided by kT. Here k is Boltzmann's constant

$$k = 1.380 \times 10^{-23} \text{ joules/degree}$$

and T is temperature in degrees Kelvin.[1] The height

[1] Temperature in degrees Kelvin is temperature in degrees Centigrade plus 273. The size of the degree is the same, but the temperature is measured from the lowest possible temperature, "absolute zero," instead of from the temperature of freezing water, which is 0° Centigrade or 273° Kelvin.

of the curve for a given energy E tells the fraction of the time that the energy of the mode will lie in some constant small range of energy ϵ, centered about E. The energy of a mode continually changes with time. Boltzmann's distribution curve says that we are less likely to find the mode with a high energy than with a low energy, and that higher and higher energies are increasingly rare.

If we use the Boltzmann distribution curve to calculate the average energy of a mode of oscillation, we find the average energy to be kT joules, regardless of the frequency of the mode. This calculation is called the *equipartition of energy,* and it is on this that Rayleigh's and Jeans's calculations were based. Since the box has an infinite number of modes of higher and higher frequency the total energy would be infinite if each mode had an energy kT.

What did Planck do that gave him the correct answer? He assumed that the Boltzmann curve was indeed correct, but that a particular mode of oscillation could not have just any energy but only particular energies. If the frequency of the mode was f it could have 0 joules of energy (no photons in the mode), hf joules (one photon in the mode), $2hf$ joules (two photons), and so on. Here h is Planck's constant.

$$h = 6.62 \times 10^{-34} \text{ joule seconds}$$

In Fig. 5 I have drawn vertical lines at energies of 0, hf, $2hg$, $3hf$, and so on. The lines go up to the Boltzmann curve, which is shown as a dotted curve. The height of the $2hf$ line is proportional to the probability that a mode of frequency f will have an energy $2hf$, and so on.

We obtain the average energy per mode in the

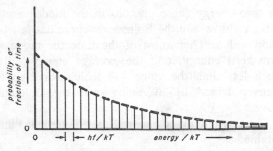

FIGURE 5

following way. We multiply the energy for each line (0, hf, $2hf$, $3hf$, and so on) by the height of the line, and we add all these products. We also add the heights of all the lines. We divide the sum of the products of height times energy by the sum of the heights. The result is the average energy.

If the frequency f is low enough so that hf/kT is very small compared with one, the lines will be very close together, as in Fig. 5. The average we obtain will be almost the same as the average that Rayleigh and Jeans obtained for the Boltzmann curve itself. But when hf/kT is unity or larger, the lines will be far apart, as shown in Fig. 6. All the lines except that

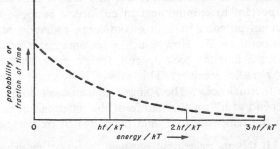

FIGURE 6

for zero energy (zero photons in the mode) are far to the right, where the Boltzmann curve has fallen to a low value. Then most of the time the mode will have zero energy, and the average energy will be much less than the value kT, which Rayleigh and Jeans obtained by averaging over the Boltzmann curve.

The actual average energy E per mode that Planck obtained is[2]

$$E = \frac{hf}{e^{hf/kT} - 1}$$

When hf/kT is very small, E is very nearly equal to kT, but once hf/kT exceeds unity, E decreases extremely rapidly with the frequency of the mode. It is because of the extremely low average energy in modes of high frequency that the total energy in the box is finite rather than infinite, as calculated by Rayleigh and Jeans.

Measuring Johnson Noise

The electromagnetic energy of each mode and the total electromagnetic energy are very important quantities, but there is another quantity that is extremely important to communication engineers. Suppose we put an antenna in a box containing radiation at a temperature T. How much electromagnetic power can the antenna pick up and, for example, transmit to a radio receiver? This power is Johnson noise, or thermal noise. The Johnson noise power does not depend at all on the nature of the antenna but only on the temperature T and the range of frequencies,

[2] If this and subsequent equations flabbergast the reader, he may find help in the Appendix.

or bandwidth, *B,* measured in cycles per second, which we include when measuring the power. This bandwidth *B* is the range of frequencies which the radio receiver or other measuring device responds to. Bandwidth is discussed at greater length in Chapter Eight of *Electrons and Waves.* The Johnson noise power *P* is

$$P = \left(\frac{hf}{e^{hf/kT} - 1} \right) B \text{ watts}$$

We have spent a good deal of time discussing the electromagnetic radiation in a closed reflecting box, because it is by considering the distribution of this radiation among the various electromagnetic resonances or modes of the box that we can compute the intensity of the radiation as a function of temperature and frequency. This intensity of radiation holds even if the box is not reflecting but has inside it various opaque, shining, or transparent objects, as long as the box and all the objects, as well as the electromagnetic radiation, are in thermal equilibrium; that is, as long as all have the same temperature, so that there is no net energy flow from one to another.

Imagine a space in which there is thermal equilibrium, a space containing various solid objects and air. On the average—that is, if we watch it over a long time—we will find that each molecule of air has a certain kinetic energy characteristic of the temperature. At any moment some molecules are moving fast and some are moving slowly, but the average speed and energy of a molecule depend only on the temperature. All the solid bodies have energies of vibration characteristic of the temperature. In solids that are conductors and contain free electrons—that is, electrons not bound to the atoms but free to move about—the electrons will have a distribution of energies characteristic of the temperature. The space inside the solid bodies as well as the space between them is filled with electromagnetic waves of various frequencies, including radio waves, heat waves, and light waves. The average energy of a wave having a particular frequency is also determined by the temperature, according to the law derived by Planck.

There is a continual transfer of energy back and forth among the molecular motion in the gas, the motions of free electrons, the vibrations of the solids, and the chaotic electromagnetic waves of various frequencies. On the average, however, each of these maintains its characteristic energy for the particular temperature involved.

Imagine that we were to examine the electromagnetic radiation inside a box held at constant temperature. We would find that electromagnetic radiation emerged from the surface of each solid body in the box, and we would find that electromagnetic radiation from other bodies fell on the surface of each body. When such a collection of bodies is in thermal equilibrium, there is an astonishingly simple fact or law of nature concerning the rate at which radiation leaves each elementary area of the surface of each body and the rate at which radiation falls on the same little part of the surface. Regardless of the physical nature of the body, the rate at which radiation leaves a given area is equal to the rate at which radiation falls on the same area. And the rate is the same for an equal area of any body regardless of the nature of the body. The rate depends only on the temperature.

If we consider a highly transparent body, we will see that most of the radiation leaving a particular square millimeter of the surface is radiation that fell on the opposite side of the body and was transmitted through it. If we consider a highly reflecting body, we will see that most of the radiation leaving a given square millimeter of the surface is simply the radiation reaching that part of the surface from other bodies and being reflected directly back again. If we consider a black object, which absorbs radiation perfectly, the radiation reaching it from other bodies is neither reflected nor transmitted; it is absorbed. Here all the radiation leaving a given square millimeter of surface is due to the thermal agitation of the charged particles near the surface.

Because no object is perfectly transparent or perfectly reflecting, some of the radiation leaving any object, transparent or reflecting, will always have originated within the object, from the thermal motion of charged particles. And, of course, some of the radiation reaching any imperfectly transmitting or reflecting object will always be absorbed into molecular motion. Since a body must always retain the same energy, radiation and absorption go hand in hand. A body which at a given temperature absorbs only a tenth of the electromagnetic energy falling on it will at the same temperature radiate only a tenth as much as a perfectly absorbing body; the rest of the quota of radiation leaving it will be transmitted or reflected radiation.

Usually we do not deal with systems of bodies which are in thermal equilibrium. We see objects surrounded by other objects at different temperatures. We can easily distinguish transparent objects, reflecting objects, and objects that absorb (and emit) radiation completely. Perfectly absorbing objects are perfectly black.

Suppose, for instance, that we have a microwave receiver so sensitive that it can measure the intensity of radio waves coming from objects at ordinary temperatures. We point the antenna of the receiver out at the world at large. The antenna will receive thermal radiation—that is, Johnson noise—from various objects. These will not necessarily be the objects at which the antenna is pointed. For instance, if we point the antenna at a mirror, the signal will come largely from whatever is reflected in the mirror. Thus, the Johnson noise received will depend chiefly on the temperature of the object we see by reflection, rather than on the temperature of the mirror. Because the mirror is not perfectly reflecting, however, some signal will come directly from the mirror. If a piece of glass is put in front of the antenna the noise will come largely from objects seen through the glass, and the Johnson noise we receive will depend on the temperature of those objects. We usually receive radiation indirectly as well as directly, from an assortment of objects at different temperatures.

Some objects, for example, steel wool or a bubble dielectric called Polyfoam to which a small amount of a conducting substance such as carbon has been added, and broken-up objects like trees and bushes, are almost completely absorbing to microwaves; they are "black" as far as microwaves are concerned. If we point our antenna at such objects, we receive from them microwave radiation or noise of an intensity that depends only on the temperature of the object and not on the temperature of its surroundings. The power we receive is simply Johnson noise

$$P = \left(\frac{hf}{e^{hf/kT} - 1}\right) B$$

where T is the temperature of the absorbing object at which the antenna is pointed.

Johnson noise is a universal phenomenon. It is not only the noise power received from an antenna in a box full of radiation or from an absorbing object; it is also the thermal power available from a resistor. Indeed, J. B. Johnson discovered Johnson noise in 1928, when he was studying the voltage fluctuations across resistors and the increase of the fluctuations with increasing temperature.

For microwave radio frequencies and for any lower frequencies, and for any but the lowest artificially produced temperatures, the following approximate expression for Johnson noise is highly accurate:

$$P = kTB$$

This expression, which corresponds to the result obtained by Rayleigh and Jeans, is frequently used in communication engineering.

The Magnitude of Johnson-Noise Power

How large is the power of Johnson noise? It is worthwhile to consider a significant example or two. Suppose that we have a microwave receiver with an antenna which is very highly directive, so that we can point it at individual objects, celestial and terrestrial. Let us say that this microwave receiver has a bandwidth of 20 megacycles, or 2×10^7 cycles per second; that is about the bandwidth of many radar receivers and of microwave systems used to transmit television. Were we to point the antenna toward the zenith we would measure noise corresponding to a temperature of less than 10 degrees Kelvin; that is, a power of less than 2.73×10^{-15} watts. If we pointed the antenna at a clump of trees at a temperature of 293 degrees Kelvin (20 degrees Centigrade, 68 degrees Fahrenheit), we would receive a noise power of about 8×10^{-13} watts. Should we point the antenna at the sun we would receive a noise power of about 1.6×10^{-12} watts, which is characteristic of a temperature of 6000 degrees Kelvin. This is the temperature we observe when we apply microwave measurements—or, indeed, visual measurements—to the sun. If, however, we were to use a 100-megacycle receiver we would receive a noise signal from the sun corresponding to a temperature of about 1,000,000 degrees Kelvin. How can this be?

A mantle of extremely hot gas, the corona, surrounds the sun. The corona is almost transparent to light waves and to microwaves; it scarcely absorbs or emits them at all. It is opaque to radio waves of longer wavelengths, however, so it both absorbs and emits such waves. One of the greatest mysteries about the sun is how the corona can be so much hotter than the surface under it.

The noise powers we have listed, and even the microwave noise power from the sun, are very minute. Yet the noise of which we have been speaking is simply electromagnetic waves emitted from a hot body, and the strong light and intense heat received from the sun are electromagnetic waves too. The noise received by the microwave receiver is so small partly because the bandwidth we have considered (a large bandwidth by radio standards) is truly minuscule compared with the bandwidth of the electromagnetic spectrum that constitutes heat and light.

In fact, visible light alone is a band of electromagnetic waves about 2.5×10^8 megacycles wide, or over ten million times as broad as the bandwidth of the microwave receiver we have discussed.

Let us return to the question of the magnitude of Johnson-noise power. Suppose, for instance, that we want to receive a microwave signal with a 20-megacycle bandwidth. Suppose that the microwave transmitter is located amid surroundings at a temperature of 20 degrees Centigrade (293 degrees Kelvin). Then if we point our receiving antenna at the transmitter we will receive about 8×10^{-13} watts, or roughly 10^{-12} watts. Suppose we want the received signal power to be a million times (10^6 times) as great as the received noise power. If this is to be so, we must receive from the transmitter a total power of 10^{-6} watts. If the total transmitted power is, for instance, one watt, we need receive only a millionth of the transmitted power in order for the received signal power to be a million times as great as the received noise power.

Unfortunately, the total noise that troubles us in microwave communication is not entirely Johnson noise received from the vicinity of the transmitter. In microwave communication and in radar most of the noise ordinarily is generated in the receiver itself, and one problem of microwave research has been to make less noisy microwave receivers. This problem has been solved brilliantly through the invention of the microwave maser, which we will discuss in the next chapter.

In order to judge a microwave receiver, we consider a hypothetical noiseless receiver which amplifies without adding noise, but which has Johnson noise corresponding to some temperature T added to its input. How great must T be if the noise in the output of the noiseless receiver is to be the same as the noise in the output of the actual receiver? This value, T, is the noise temperature of the actual receiver. In the very best microwave receivers using traveling wave tubes, T is about 600°. A similar performance is attained in superheterodyne microwave receivers.

The Superheterodyne Receiver

A superheterodyne receiver is a particularly apt device to discuss in connection with quantum noise, because it can be used in receiving light signals as well as radio waves. (The operation of a superheterodyne receiver is explained in some detail in Chapter Eight of *Electrons and Waves;* here I will give only a brief description.) Suppose that to a small sinusoidal signal we wish to amplify we add a sinusoidal signal of larger amplitude, a signal with a slightly different frequency. The combined signal looks sinusoidal, but its power has a small variation with time. This variation in power is sinusoidal. If the frequencies of the small signal and the large signal are f_1 and f_2, the frequency f_p with which the power of the combined signal varies is

$$f_p = f_2 - f_1$$

If we put the combined signal into a device that responds to power, the output of the device will be a sinusoidal signal of frequency f_p. The over-all effect is that a small input signal of frequency f_1 produces a small output signal of frequency $f_p = f_2 - f_1$. We can amplify this signal of frequency f_p by using transistors or vacuum tubes, and we can easily measure the amplified signal. For f_2, the frequency of the *local oscillator* of the superheterodyne receiver, we choose a value that makes f_p easy to amplify. As the device responding to the power of the input signal we can use at radio frequencies a solid-state diode (see Chapter V). When the input signal is light, we can use a photoemitter as the device responding to power, for the rate of emission of electrons from the photoemitter is proportional to the power of the light falling on it.

The superheterodyne receiver provides a convenient means for amplifying signals, because we can choose an *intermediate frequency* f_p at which amplification is easy. As an alternative, we can, of course, amplify the signal at its original frequency f_1, using, for instance, a maser. A good maser amplifier adds to the signal and the Johnson noise picked up by the antenna, a noise corresponding to a frequency of only a few degrees Kelvin. Moreover, there are masers that can amplify extremely high frequencies—light waves as well as microwaves. Such *optical masers* are called *lasers*.

Here we come to a curious question concerning noise. The correct quantum-mechanical expression for noise power shows that the noise power for a given bandwidth and temperature decreases as the frequency f of the signal is increased. Does this mean that at optical frequencies noise will be less serious than it is at microwave frequencies? It does not. Remember that electromagnetic radiation comes in discrete units of energy, called photons. Each has an energy hf. Thus, for higher frequencies the energy per photon is greater, and for a given power the higher the frequency the fewer photons per second the signal will contain. We expect weak signals of extremely high frequency to be in some sense "lumpy."

Some receivers for electromagnetic waves in the optical range show just this effect. Consider a super-heterodyne receiver that has, for its power-sensitive device, a photoemitter producing one output electron for each photon that strikes it. A weak, modulated electromagnetic signal of optical frequency will strike this photoemitter together with a strong sinusoidal light wave having a slightly different frequency (say, a light wave generated by a laser[3]). The output current from the photoemitter will be a lower-frequency signal. This lower-frequency signal contains what is called *shot noise,* corresponding to the uneven or random production of electrons by the individual photons of the light. When we amplify the intermediate frequency signal we must amplify this shot noise as well. As the frequency goes up there are fewer quanta per second for a given light power and hence fewer electrons per second, and the shot noise becomes larger compared with the output signal.

The Limitations of an Ideal Amplifier

There is another way of looking at the quantum-mechanical aspects of noise. Suppose we consider a mass supported by a spring. If we give the mass a push it will oscillate back and forth. Quantum mechanics tells us that we cannot measure both the momentum of the mass and its position with complete accuracy. If we make arrangements to measure the momentum very accurately, we must be un-

[3] A laser is a device that can generate and amplify sinusoidal light waves. Chapter IV discusses the laser.

certain about the position. If we arrange to measure the position very accurately, we must be uncertain of the momentum. This is Heisenberg's uncertainty principle, which we discussed in Chapter I.

The electrical analogue of a mass supported by a spring is a resonant circuit consisting of a coil or inductor connected to a capacitor.[4] In a resonant circuit, momentum corresponds to the current in the inductor multiplied by the inductance of the inductor, and position corresponds to the electric charge on the capacitor. Heisenberg's uncertainty principle tells us that if we measure the current very accurately we cannot measure the charge very accurately; or, if we measure the charge very accurately we cannot measure the current very accurately. If the oscillation in a resonant circuit is strong, the uncertainty in the measurement will be small compared to the amplitude of the oscillation, but this is not so for very weak oscillations.

Suppose that we connect the input of a high-gain linear amplifier across the capacitor of an electrical resonator and observe the output waveform on an oscilloscope.[5] The amplitude of the output wave will be proportional to the charge on the capacitor. We can measure this amplitude very accurately as a function of time from the trace on the oscilloscope. We can measure the slope of the oscilloscope trace very accurately as a function of time. This slope is proportional to the rate of change of the charge, which is the current. Hence, by measuring the slope of the oscilloscope trace as a function of time we can measure the current accurately as a function of time. Does this violate the quantum-mechanical un-

[4] See *Electrons and Waves,* pages 169–173.
[5] See *Electrons and Waves,* pages 68–71.

certainty principle? It would if the displacement of the oscilloscope trace were merely a large constant, which we call the voltage gain of the amplifier, times the charge on the capacitor. But if the amplifier output is determined by noise as well as by the input signal, the oscilloscope trace does not accurately represent the charge on the capacitor to which the input of the amplifier is connected, and all may be well.

In fact, all can be and is well. The output of the best possible linear amplifier contains just the expected amount of noise. The amount of noise power P_0 in the output of the best possible linear amplifier is

$$P_0 = G\left(\frac{hf}{e^{hf/kT} - 1}\right) B + (G - 1)\, hfB$$

Here G is the power gain of the amplifier—the factor by which the amplifier output power is greater than the input power. The first term of this expression is simply amplified Johnson noise, and T is the temperature, or effective temperature, of the noise source acting as an input to the amplifier. It is the second term that deserves our present attention. If the output of the amplifier is to be large enough so that we can measure it accurately, the power gain G must be large. But if G is large, $G - 1$ is large and the term $(G - 1)hfB$ corresponds to a large noise. We are uncertain just what part of the output of the amplifier is due to this noise and which part of the output is due to the input to the amplifier, that is, the charge on the capacitor. If $G = 1$, the added noise is zero, but the amplifier doesn't amplify, and the output is so small that quantum-mechanical effects keep us from measuring it accurately. In fact, the accuracy of deducing the input from the most accurate possible measurement of the output turns out not to depend on the gain G. The uncertainty concerning the current and charge of the resonator fits exactly that required by quantum mechanics.

No linear amplifier can have less noise power in its output than the power P_0 given by the above expression. The superheterodyne receiver described a little earlier would give this minimum noise power if the photoemitter actually produced one electron per photon, and if the light wave from the laser was very powerful, and if the amplifier following the photoemitter added negligible noise. The noise in the output of some maser amplifiers is only a few times that of an ideal amplifier.

In this chapter we have seen how the ideas of quantum mechanics are essential in computing Johnson or thermal noise, which is a fundamental limitation in communication. Planck's idea that modes of oscillation can have only discrete energies is essential for computation of the noise received by an antenna or the noise from a resistor. Heisenberg's uncertainty principle is essential to an understanding of the limitations of an ideal amplifier—how accurately such an amplifier can make extremely small signals visible and measurable, whether those signals be thermal noise or weak signals from some far transmitter.

This may seem to associate quantum mechanics only with troubles and limitations. But quantum effects are the essential ingredient in the maser amplifier, the least noisy amplifier that exists. In the next chapter we will see why.

Chapter III

MASERS

Isaac Newton's decomposition of white sunlight into components of different colors, which could be recombined to give white light again, was one of the most beautiful experiments in the history of science. Newton carried out his experiments in the late seventeenth century, but it was not until the early nineteenth century that Joseph von Frauenhofer observed that there are dark lines crossing the spectra of the sun and stars. By measuring the wavelengths of the dark lines with diffraction gratings, Frauenhofer showed them to be precisely measurable features of the light emitted by various physical sources.

By 1859, Gustav R. Kirchhoff and Robert Wilhelm Bunsen had related many spectral lines (or wavelengths) to the particular elements producing them. They also had shown clearly that a vapor that emits a certain wavelength or frequency of light will absorb light of precisely the same frequency. For instance, hot sodium vapor produces a bright yellow line with a wavelength of 5.9×10^{-5} cm; you can see this if you throw salt in a flame and look at the spectrum. Sodium vapor will absorb light of the same frequency. It is absorption of light by the relatively cooler upper layers of the atmosphere of a star that accounts for the dark spectral lines that Frauenhofer studied.

Spectroscopy was one of the most powerful tools of physics in the nineteenth and early twentieth centuries. Observations were pushed to the long invisible infrared wavelengths and to the short invisible ultraviolet wavelengths. Frequencies of emission (and absorption) of the various elements were identified, and numerically related series of spectral lines or frequencies were discovered.

Spectroscopy was a powerful measuring tool, but it was not until 1913, when Niels Bohr successfully applied quantum ideas to the atom, that frequencies of absorption and emission could be calculated numerically from elementary data—that is, from Newton's laws of motion, the law of attraction of electric charges, the charges and masses of the electron and the proton, and Planck's constant h. Physicists' understanding of the structure and behavior of atoms, molecules, and ions[1] is deep and complicated. Crude reasoning from classical physical laws has been replaced by the truly quantum-mechanical wave equations of Irwin Schroedinger and P. A. M. Dirac. Understanding has extended to the properties of crystals, which are orderly arrays of atoms (as we will see in the final chapter of this book, which deals with semiconductor devices). The radiation from single atoms, molecules, and ions has continued, however, to be vitally important. The quantum-mechanical details of such radiation can be exceedingly complicated, but there is an over-all quantum-mechanical description which is universally useful.

[1] An ion is an atom or molecule which has lost or gained one or more electrons and hence has an electric charge.

Energy Levels

A violin string has certain particular modes or patterns of oscillation, each of which has its particular frequency of vibration, its *resonant frequency*. So has an organ pipe. Similarly, a box with reflecting walls can contain various patterns of electromagnetic radiation, each with its particular frequency. We considered this in the preceding chapter.

Quantum mechanics tells us that an atom or a molecule or an ion can exist in any one of various *states*. Each state can be thought of as a mode of motion or vibration of the constituent particles of the atom or molecule or ion. Each state has some particular energy. There is a state that has the lowest energy of any, E_0. This is called the *ground state*. Other states are called *excited states*. We can represent the energies of these states as shown in Fig. 7.

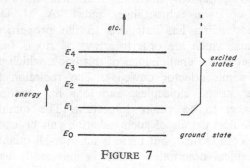

FIGURE 7

Here the vertical distances between the lines represent differences in energy. The lines in such a diagram, which show the energies of the various states, are called *energy levels,* and *energy level* also is used interchangeably with *state* in referring to a particular condition of an atom or molecule or ion. In Fig. 7, the energy levels are labeled E_0, E_1, E_2, etc. In many diagrams a more complicated labeling scheme is used, which reflects the physical nature of the state (in an atom, perhaps what electron is in what orbit or level). The physical details of the states are very complicated, and here we will merely take it for granted that an atom or a molecule or an ion does have many possible states, each with its own particular energy.

Induced Energy Level Transitions

Why does an atom or molecule or ion go from one state or energy level to a state of lower or higher energy? If an atom or molecule or ion is uninfluenced by anything else, and if it is in any state but the ground state, it eventually will go spontaneously to some state of lower energy. The energy difference between the states will be given off as radiation. An atom or molecule or ion may, however, stay in an excited state for days or even years. Usually, it is something other than such *spontaneous emission* that causes a transition between energy levels. In a gas, a collision between particles or with the wall of the containing vessel can cause a transition from one energy level to another. Electromagnetic radiation also can cause transitions, and we will be particularly interested in transitions induced by the electromagnetic radiation.

An electromagnetic field can give energy to an atom or a molecule or an ion and cause it to go to a higher energy level. For instance, absorption of a photon of frequency f can cause an atom or molecule or ion to go from a state of energy E_m to a state of energy E_n if

$$E_m - E_n = hf$$

Similarly, an electromagnetic field can cause an atom or molecule or ion to go from a state of energy E_m to a state of energy E_n by emitting a photon of frequency f given by

$$f = \frac{E_m - E_n}{h}$$

A Fundamental Explanation of Spectra

An electromagnetic field of a particular strength is just as likely to cause a transition from the higher energy state to the lower energy state as it is to cause a transition from the lower energy state to the higher energy state. Here we have the quantum-mechanical explanation of the bright and dark lines of spectroscopy. The pattern of energy levels is different for different elements. For a given element the differences between the various energy levels are proportional to the frequencies of the spectral lines the element produces when it is excited, and the absorption lines the element produces when light passes through it.

In order to understand fully the absorption of energy at particular frequencies when bright light passes through a gas (when the light of the sun passes through the sun's atmosphere, for instance) we have to consider one further thing, the fractions of atoms, or molecules, or ions that are in various states. Let us consider an atom, molecule, or ion which has two states or energy levels whose energy difference corresponds to a frequency f. Strong electromagnetic radiation of frequency f can quickly cause or *induce* a transition either from the lower level to the higher level or from the higher level to the lower level. If a greater fraction of the atoms or molecules or ions is in the lower level then the radiation will cause more transitions from the lower level to the higher level than from the higher level to the lower level. For instance, if there were *no* atoms or molecules or ions in the higher level then the radiation clearly couldn't cause any transitions from the higher level to the lower level. If there were more atoms or molecules or ions in the higher level than in the lower level radiation would cause more transitions from the higher level to the lower level than from the lower level to the higher level. Thus, if there are more atoms or molecules or ions in the lower than in the higher level there will be more transitions up than down, and on the average the gas of atoms, molecules, or ions will absorb energy. If there were more in the higher than in the lower level the gas would radiate energy, and this energy would add to the electromagnetic radiation causing the transitions.

The Boltzmann Distribution Curve

The atoms, or molecules, or ions of a gas can gain or lose energy through collisions or through interaction with radiation. What determines the relative numbers of the atoms or molecules or ions of a gas that will be in various energy levels? Ordinarily, the Boltzmann distribution curve of Fig. 4 determines this. This curve says that for a gas at a given temperature a given atom or molecule or ion will spend some larger fraction of its time in a state of lower energy than in a state of higher energy. Or, for a gas consisting of many atoms or molecules or ions, it says that at a given time more will be in a lower level than in a higher level. Thus, when the number of atoms or molecules or ions in various levels is determined by the Boltzmann curve, a gas will absorb part of the radiation passing through it rather than adding energy to that radiation. And, except in unusual circumstances, the Boltzmann curve does determine the number of atoms or molecules or ions in each energy level.

The Application of Microwave Spectroscopy to Communications Technology

Quantum mechanics added something of great importance to spectroscopy—a fundamental explanation of spectra. Another great addition came from the growth of microwave technology before and during World War II and the training of physicists in this new technology through their wartime work on radar. At the end of the war, a host of physicists went back to university work equipped with the powerful new tool of microwave technology. They proceeded to apply it to an old field—spectroscopy. But, this was not the spectroscopy of light, which has a frequency of over 10^{14} cycles per second, but microwave spectroscopy, with frequencies of around 10^{10} cycles per second.

One of the physicists who turned to microwave spectroscopy was Charles H. Townes, who then worked at the Bell Telephone Laboratories and at this writing is Provost of the Massachusetts Institute of Technology. In 1948, some people did not see that microwave spectroscopy would become highly relevant to communications technology. It seemed more relevant to pure physics, and, in 1948, Townes went to Columbia University to continue his work on microwave spectroscopy.

In 1951, while he was sitting on a park bench in Washington, D. C., waiting for an appointment, the concept of the maser came to Townes. The relevance of microwave spectroscopy to communication was established so resoundingly as to result in the award of the Nobel Prize to Townes, together with Nikolai G. Basor and Alexander M. Prokhorov of the Lebedev Institute, Moscow, in 1964 for "fundamental work in the field of quantum mechanics which has led to the construction of oscillators and amplifiers based on the maser-laser principle."

The first maser (Microwave Amplification by Stimulated Electromagnetic Emission), which Townes, James P. Gordon, and Zieger described in 1954, made use of two of the lower-energy levels of the molecules of gaseous ammonia. The difference in energy between these two levels corresponds to a frequency of 23,870 megacycles, or a wavelength of 1.25 cm. In ammonia at room temperature a distribution of molecules among energy levels according to the Boltzmann curve is such that about 3 per cent of the molecules are in each of the two states or energy levels used in ammonia maser. Most happily, the molecules in the two different states have different electrical properties. Those in the lower-energy state tend to move from a region of lower electric field to a region of higher electric field. Those in the higher-energy state tend to move from a region of higher electric field to a region of lower electric field. Gordon, Zieger, and Townes used this phenomenon in separating the upper- from the lower-state molecules.

Imagine four long metallic electrodes, as shown end-on in Fig. 8. Suppose we connect the left and

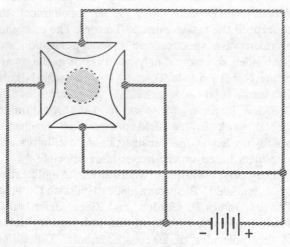

FIGURE 8

right electrodes to the negative pole of a battery, and the top and bottom electrodes to the positive pole of a battery. Right at the center point between the four electrodes there will be no electric field. As we go farther away from the center point the positive and negative electrodes are closer together and the electric field is stronger. Hence, if ammonia molecules are placed between the electrodes, the higher-energy molecules are pushed toward the center, and the lower-energy molecules are drawn outward.

Suppose that we let a narrow, low-density beam of ammonia molecules escape from a container,

shown at the left of Fig. 9. Both high-energy and
low-energy molecules will start to drift through the
electrode system of Fig. 8. But the low-energy molecules will be drawn toward the electrodes and lost,
while the high-energy molecules will be forced toward the center and held in a narrow beam. Thus,
there will emerge from the right end of the electrode
system a narrow beam consisting of high-energy, ex

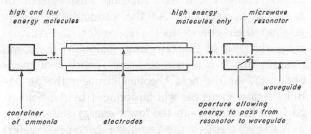

FIGURE 9

cited molecules only, together with some molecules
in other, irrelevant energy levels.

In the ammonia maser the beam of high-energy
molecules passes into an electromagnetic resonator[2]
tuned to the transition frequency between the higher-
energy state and the lower-energy state—that is, to a
frequency of 23,870 megacycles. An electromagnetic
wave of this frequency could give energy to ammonia
molecules by transferring them from the lower- to
the higher-energy state—but, initially there *are* no

[2] An electromagnetic resonator is a conducting box or
other structure in which an electromagnetic wave or oscillation of a particular resonant frequency can exist. A stretched
string which can vibrate with a particular resonant frequency
is a mechanical analogue of an electromagnetic resonator.
Resonators are discussed in some detail in Chapter Seven of
Electrons and Waves.

molecules in the lower-energy state. Or it could take energy from ammonia molecules by transferring them from the higher-energy state to the lower-energy state. This it can do, for the molecules are in the higher-energy state.

Now we will remember from Chapter II that although electromagnetic energy of a given frequency comes in discrete amounts called photons, any number of photons can exist in one wave-pattern or mode of a resonator. As the ammonia molecules give up their energy to the resonator, the electromagnetic field in the resonator maintains the same pattern, but it becomes stronger (consists of more photons). As the field becomes stronger the probability that a molecule will be induced by the field to go from the higher- to the lower-energy state during its passage through the resonator becomes greater. Thus, the electromagnetic field in the resonator grows in strength until the fraction of molecules transferred to the lower level during passage through the resonator becomes substantial.

We will remember that an electromagnetic field can act either to transfer a molecule from a higher level to a lower level, or from a lower level to a higher level. The ammonia molecules entering the resonator are all in the higher level, so initially all the transitions are from the higher level to the lower level, and this process adds energy to the electromagnetic field. If, however, the molecules have stayed in the resonator too long very many will have been transferred to the lower level, and the field can then transfer these back to the higher level again. This process takes energy from the electromagnetic field. Thus, leaving the molecules in the resonator too long can decrease rather than increase the total energy derived from the molecules.

Some of the energy given up by the ammonia molecules is dissipated in a flow of electric current along the imperfectly conducting walls of the resonator. This dissipation of energy is just like the loss of power due to the electrical resistance of any resonant circuit. Some of the energy can be allowed to leak out of an aperture in the resonator and into a waveguide, as shown in Fig. 9, and so furnish a useful microwave output.

Ammonia masers have very low power outputs—around a billionth of a watt. Their frequency of oscillation is very stable, varying with time by a few parts in 10^{10}. Hence, ammonia masers are useful as very precise frequency sources or "clocks." The excited ammonia molecules could give up their energy to a traveling wave rather than to a standing wave, and so cause amplification of the wave. Excited ammonia molecules can interact with only a narrow range of frequencies, however; such an amplifier can amplify only a very narrow band or range of frequencies. Further, as we have noted, the power output of the ammonia maser is very small.

The Three-Level Solid-State Maser

Cannot the maser principle be applied in some other way, in order to overcome these difficulties and give a useful amplifier? In 1956 N. Bloembergen proposed a method, the three-level solid-state maser, which we will now discuss. H. E. D. Scovil, G. Feher, and H. Seidel first announced the successful operation of such a device in 1957. C. Makhov, C. Kikuchi, J. Lambe, and R. W. Terhune, in 1958, first described a maser using a pink ruby, in which the active material is chromium (which gives the pink color) in a crystal of aluminum oxide. In the crystal the chromium, like the aluminum, is present as a triply charged ion—three of its electrons are lost to the other oxygen atoms. In general, the behavior of atoms, or molecules, or ions in a solid is much more complicated than in a gas, but in the three-level solid-state maser the active material (the chromium ions in ruby, for instance) form so small a fraction of the total crystal that they are effectively isolated from one another. They act individually, just as do the molecules in the gaseous ammonia used in the ammonia maser.

In 1896 a Dutch physicist, Peter Zeeman, no-

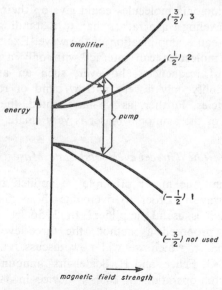

FIGURE 10

ticed that some spectral lines in the presence of a magnetic field are split into two lines of different frequency. The splitting of the spectral line corresponds, of course, to a splitting of a single energy level into two energy levels by the magnetic field. This effect is vital in the operation of the three-level solid-state maser. It makes it possible to tune such a maser so that it can oscillate or amplify at a frequency dependent on the magnetic field. Figure 10 shows how the energy levels that are important in the operation of a ruby maser change with magnetic field.[3] The energy difference between the upper two levels, marked (3/2) and 3, and (1/2) and 2, can be increased steadily by increasing the magnetic field.

The energies between any of these levels is small compared with thermal energy at room temperature. At room temperature thermal energy will cause rapid interchanges up and down between all of these energy levels. According to the Boltzmann distribution curve, at room temperature nearly the same number of ions will be in each of the levels. But if we lower the temperature of the crystal from 293°K (20°C, or room temperature) to around 4°K, thermal energy will cause transfers from one level to another at a much slower rate. Further, for this temperature the Boltzmann curve tells us that there will be appreciably more chromium ions in the lower levels than in the higher levels.

We have noted that a strong electromagnetic field of suitable frequency will cause rapid transitions between energy levels. In the three-level solid-state maser such a strong field, called a *pump* field, is

[3] The exact nature of the curves depends on the orientation of the crystal in the magnetic field.

used. Its frequency is chosen to correspond to the energy difference between the 3 level and the 1 level. Thus, this field causes rapid transitions up and down between these levels through the absorption and emission of energy. Shortly, the numbers of ions in the 3 and the 1 levels will be equal.

What about the 2 level? A few ions will make spontaneous transitions from the 3 level to the 2 level, and a few from the 2 level to the 1 level. Thermal energy will cause a few transitions among levels. It turns out that the 2 level can have fewer ions in it than the 1 and 3 levels, which have equal numbers. The average time it takes for an ion to go from the 2 level to the 1 level by giving energy to vibrations of the crystal is shorter than the average time for a transition from the 3 level to the 2 level. There is a tendency for more widely separated levels to undergo spontaneous transitions more quickly than levels which are closer together in energy.

The important thing is that by pumping with a suitable electromagnetic field it is possible to attain a condition in which there are more ions in the higher 3 level than in the lower 2 energy level. This situation is contrary to what we find in crystals held at any positive temperature and not exposed to electromagnetic fields. Always in such crystals the Boltzmann distribution curve tells us that we are at least a little more likely to find an ion or atom or molecule or electron in a lower-energy level than in a higher-energy level. Hence, the peculiar condition in which more ions are in a higher than a lower-energy level is called a *population inversion* and is said to correspond to a negative temperature (which would, according to the Boltzmann distribution curve, put ions or atoms or molecules in higher rather than lower-energy levels).

Having obtained a population inversion, so that there are more ions in the higher-energy level 3 than in the lower energy level 2, we need merely, as in the ammonia maser, put the crystal in a resonant cavity or in a suitable structure supporting a traveling wave[4] in order to obtain oscillation or amplification. But in doing this effectively there are formidable problems.

Problems in Using a Population Inversion

One problem is that of designing the circuit so that it will function effectively both at the frequency of amplification or oscillation and at the pumping frequency, where the electromagnetic energy necessary to achieve the population inversion must be supplied. Suppose that we do succeed in putting a ruby in a circuit that will propagate a traveling electromagnetic wave which we wish to amplify, and that we also succeed in applying a pump field of a different frequency. The device will amplify a wave traveling through it in either direction. This undirected amplification is undesirable, however, because a little of the amplified wave can be reflected back toward the input and amplified on the way. An amplifier amplifying waves in both directions is likely to oscillate.

Another important problem is to achieve a suitably broad bandwidth. In the best traveling-wave

[4] As the wave of Fig. 2 moves to the right, it constitutes a traveling wave. Such a wave can travel through space, or along a wire, or through a pipe. Traveling waves are discussed in Chapter Six of *Electrons and Waves*.

maser amplifiers the wave travels through a complicated structure, in which rods, in a comblike array,
project from one narrow wall of a rectangular metal
tube or waveguide, as shown in Fig. 11. Electro-

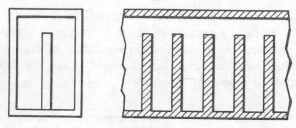

FIGURE 11

magnetic waves of sufficiently high frequency can
travel through a rectangular waveguide, but waves
of lower frequency cannot. The size of the waveguide used in the maser is so chosen that the pump
frequency, which is higher than the frequency to be
amplified, could travel through the tube or waveguide even if the rods of the comb were not present,
and the rods of the comb do not impede its travel.
Waves of the signal frequency to be amplified could
not travel through the waveguide if the rods were
not there. The rods make it possible for the lower-
frequency signal to go through the small rectangular
waveguide, and the energy of the signal wave is
highest near the rods. Slabs of ruby are put along
the sides of the comb, as shown in Fig. 12, and a
magnetic field is applied in the direction of the rods,
as indicated by the arrows.

Ordinarily, when an electromagnetic wave passes
a point, the electric and magnetic fields alternate in
direction at the point, passing through zero in be-

tween, like the sine curve of Fig. 2. Such waves are said to be *linearly* polarized. In the waveguide at a point halfway between the base or attached ends of the rods forming the teeth of the comb, and a little off the center line of the comb, the magnetic field of an electromagnetic signal traveling along the comb is *circularly* polarized. By this we mean that as the electromagnetic signal wave travels past this point, its magnetic field remains constant in magnitude but rotates in direction. Further, the direction of rotation is reversed if the direction in which the electromagnetic wave travels along the comb is reversed.

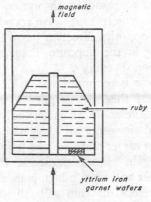

FIGURE 12

Now, some non-conducting crystals are strongly magnetic, as iron is. We say that these crystals have *ferro-magnetic* properties. Yttrium iron garnet is such a crystal. When this substance is put in a steady magnetic field, it will absorb energy from a microwave rotating magnetic field having one direction of rotation but will be little affected by a field of the same frequency of rotation that is rotating in the opposite direction. The frequency at which the absorption of energy is greatest depends on the strength of the steady magnetic field.

This phenomenon can be used in order to absorb power from and hence weaken waves propagating in one direction along the comblike structure without absorbing power from waves traveling in the opposite direction. Small wafers of yttrium iron garnet are placed near the base of the comb structure, at the points at which the magnetic field is circularly polarized. A wave traveling along the comb in one direction has a magnetic field which rotates in such a direction as to result in absorption of energy by the yttrium iron garnet. A wave traveling along the comb in the opposite direction has a magnetic field which rotates in the opposite direction and causes little absorption of energy.

Finally, there is the matter of making a traveling-wave maser of this sort amplify a wide range or band of frequencies. If we make the steady applied magnetic field the same all along the length of the ruby of such a maser amplifier and adjust its strength for greatest gain at one particular frequency, the maser amplifier will have a high gain at one particular frequency, but the gain will fall to a low value if the signal frequency is changed a little. We can, however, get a constant gain over a range of frequencies by changing the strength of the magnetic field from point to point along the length of the structure. Thus, some portions of the length will amplify one range of frequencies, and other portions will amplify another range. The gain will be less than that of a narrow-band maser with a magnetic field which has the same strength everywhere along the structure, but the bandwidth or range of frequencies over which the device will amplify is greater.

Efficiency in a Maser Amplifier

A maser of this sort is used in the A.T.&T. satellite earth station at Andover, Maine, for receiving signals from the TELSTAR communication satellite, and from other communication satellites. Some data concerning this maser are:

Center frequency (of signal)	4,170 mc
Bandwidth	25 mc
Gain	28 db (630 times)[5]
Pump frequency	30,175 mc
Pump power	.070 watt
Temperature of ruby	4.2°K
Noise temperature, T_n	3.5°K

As we noted in Chapter II, the noise temperature of an amplifier is a convenient measure of the noise it adds to the signal it amplifies. A noise temperature of 3.5°K seems very low compared with the noise temperature of around 600°K that we obtain with a good traveling-wave tube amplifier. But how near is it to the ideal limit?

In Chapter II we saw that the noise power output P_0 of an ideal amplifier—that is, the very best amplifier the laws of nature would allow us to make—is

$$P_0 = G \left(\frac{hf}{e^{hf/kT} - 1} \right) B + (G - 1) \, hfB$$

[5] db is the universally used abbreviation for decibel or decibels. If the power output of an amplifier is G times the power input, the gain is $10 \log_{10} G$ decibels.

The first term is amplified Johnson or thermal noise.

Let us assume that T is zero; then none of the noise output is amplified Johnson noise, but it all is noise generated in the ideal amplifier. Let us assume that G is so large that $G-1$ differs from G by a negligible fraction. Then for the ideal receiver, closely enough

$$P_0 = GhfB$$

For an actual receiver of noise temperature T_n, the noise power output will, by definition, be equal to amplified thermal noise corresponding to the temperature T_n.

$$P_0 = G\left(\frac{hf}{e^{hf/kT_n}-1}\right)B$$

Thus, for an ideal receiver T_n must have such a value as to make the "equivalent amplified thermal noise" of the second expression equal the actual noise of the ideal receiver, so that

$$hf = \frac{hf}{e^{hf/kT_n}-1}$$

Or

$$T_n = \frac{hf}{k\ln 2}$$

Let us now consider the noise temperature of the ideal receiver at the frequency 4,170 mc, the operating frequency of the maser described above.

$$h = 6.62 \times 10^{-34} \text{ joule seconds}$$
$$f = 4.17 \times 10^9$$
$$k = 1.38 \times 10^{-23} \text{ joules/degree}$$
$$\ln 2 = .693$$
$$T_n = 0.288°K$$
$$\ln 2 = .693$$

Thus, the noise temperature of the maser described, 3.5°K, is about twelve times as great as the noise temperature of the very best linear amplifier that the laws of quantum mechanics could ever allow us to make. This is excellent performance. Could we attain better?

Part of the disparity is due to thermal noise associated with the electrical resistance of the comb-like circuit. Part is due to an imperfect inversion of levels; that is, to the fact that level 2 of Fig. 10 is not completely empty. If a maser had no circuit losses, and if the lower of the levels whose energy difference corresponds to the signal frequency (level 2 of Fig. 10) were completely empty, the maser would behave as an ideal linear amplifier and, at a frequency of 4,170 mc, its noise temperature would be 0.288°K. It is certainly possible to go somewhat further in this direction.

Chapter IV

LASERS

A laser (Light Amplification by Stimulated Electromagnetic Radiation) is a maser operating at the extremely high frequencies and short wavelengths of light. At first, lasers were called optical masers, and sometimes still are, but the term laser appears to have won out, particularly in the press.

There have been few advances that have created as much furor as the laser did. Hundreds of government contracts were let, seemingly to every Tom, Dick, or Harry who applied, to reinvent, develop, and seek uses for this glamorous new tool. The newspaper stories were myriad. Happily, contracts are now being let more thoughtfully, and the news stories are perhaps better informed. We have had time to sit back and think about lasers and even to wonder why they excited so much interest.

The principle of operation of the laser is the same as that of the maser. What is so new, then? The difference in the laser—and it *is* something new under the sun—is *coherent* light.

The nature of electromagnetic radiation, we have tried to show in this book, is such that any number of photons can exist in one mode or pattern of oscillation. This mode may be a standing wave pattern of oscillation in the resonant cavity or resonator of a vacuum-tube oscillator or a maser oscillator. Or the mode may be a traveling wave—a flow of electromagnetic energy through a waveguide or from a radio antenna. In such coherent radiation the electromagnetic field at each point varies sinusoidally with time, with a single frequency and a constant amplitude.

Clearly, the contrary of coherent radiation must be incoherent radiation. As an example, the total radiation from a large number of sources of radiation differing in frequency and going on and off with time is incoherent radiation. Incoherent radiation may consist of a narrow band of frequencies, as does a spectral line, but it never consists of a single frequency, and it fluctuates rapidly in amplitude. Thus, incoherent radiation is noisy.

In the very first radio telegraph transmitters electromagnetic waves were generated by a sequence of somewhat irregularly timed sparks, each of which produced a short burst of radiation. The resulting electromagnetic radiation was incoherent. It spread over a band of frequencies, and its intensity fluctuated with time. When one tuned a radio receiver to the signal from such a transmitter, one heard dots and dashes as short and long bursts of noise.

One of the greatest advances in radio was the replacement of incoherent spark transmitters with coherent or cw (continuous wave) transmitters. The devices of this progress were Valdemar Poulsen's oscillating arc (in 1903) and Ernst F. W. Alexanderson's alternator (in 1907). But it was the audion or vacuum tube of Lee De Forest (1873–1961) that enabled us to generate, amplify, and modulate coherent radio signals with great flexibility and ease. The vacuum tube made both radio telephony and television possible.

In all the centuries between the time the world began and the invention of the laser, light was incoherent. The light we receive from the sun comes from a host of atoms, molecules, and ions, each excited to radiate by heat, and each radiating independently. The incoherent white light of the sun, of a flame, of the filament of an electric light bulb, contains a broad band of frequencies corresponding to many colors. The light from a neon sign is made up of narrow ranges of frequencies lying about the spectral lines of neon, but it is incoherent.

Thus, the laser is revolutionary in that it produces something entirely new under the sun: coherent light. A beam of light from a laser can travel in a simple, narrow pattern of radiation, contrasted with the broader beam of a searchlight. The laser enables us to apply all the techniques of radio transmission: modulation, frequency changing, and amplification, to communication or radar systems which use the very-high-frequency electromagnetic radiation called light, rather than the lower-frequency electromagnetic radiation called radio waves.

Uses of Coherent Light

We may well ask, then, what new things does the laser enable us to do? So far, the laser has proved to be a powerful tool with few important applications. It has found some use in short-range radar. Laser beams have been used in eye surgery to heat small portions of the retina, but other light sources can be used for this purpose. Laser beams can burn a hole through a razor blade, but it is cheaper to use a drill. Early in the game it was suggested that laser beams might be used to burn up approaching missiles, but this laudable application appears to be impractical. It has been suggested also that laser beams might be used to vaporize matter and raise the vapor to a very high temperature to provide rocket propulsion of increased effectiveness for space travel. The very precise frequency has aroused speculation that laser beams could be used to cause certain chemical reactions. Laser beams have been pictured as a possible tool for communication between spaceships, but the very narrowness of the beams would work against this application.

To me, the most exciting proposal is to send many voice and TV signals over long distances with lasers. One could do this by guiding the light from the laser through a buried pipe by means of a sequence of lenses and amplifying the light periodically by means of laser amplifiers. Many practical problems will have to be solved before such communication becomes economical. Unlike the transistor, which fitted naturally into all sorts of applications and already has revolutionized each field of electronics into which it fitted, the laser is a revolutionary new tool which at present has no widespread, practical, economic use. Perhaps, then, the best thing to do is to examine the nature and properties of lasers and to leave applications to the future, science fiction, and the newspapers.

Properties of Lasers

We have noted that a laser makes use of the same fundamental phenomena and principles as does a maser—but in a range of frequencies roughly 100,-000 times higher (or wavelengths a hundred-thousandth as long) as the microwaves used in communication and radar. Since the differences between masers and lasers hinge upon this difference in frequency and wavelength, it seems worthwhile to tabulate some typical values. This has been done in Table I.

TABLE I

Description	Wavelengths cm	Frequency cps
Long microwaves	15	2×10^9
Short microwaves	3	10^{10}
Long millimeter waves	1	3×10^{10}
Short millimeter waves	$10-1$	3×10^{11}
Long infrared	$10-2$	3×10^{12}
Short infrared	$10-4$	3×10^{14}
Longest visible red	7.2×10^{-5}	4.2×10^{14}
Shortest visible violet	4.0×10^{-5}	7.5×10^{14}

Lasers have been made to operate over the range of wavelength from around .01 cm (long infrared) through the visible spectrum into ultraviolet radiation of wavelength as short as 2.5×10^{-5} cm.

Because of the short wavelength and high frequency of the infrared and visible parts of the electromagnetic spectrum, the construction and properties of lasers differ from the construction and properties of masers, even though the fundamental principle of operation is the same. One striking difference is the amount of energy that a single atom or molecule or ion gives to the electromagnetic field. This quantity of energy is, of course, the energy of a photon. We will remember from Chapter I that this energy is Planck's constant h times the frequency. Let us compare the energies for the ammonia maser, for which the frequency is 2.39×10^{10} cycles per second, and the ruby laser, for which the frequency is about 4.32×10^{14} cycles per second. The energy contributed by the ammonia molecule is 1.53×10^{-23} joules; that contributed by the chromium ion in the ruby laser is 2.7×10^{-19} joules—over 10,000 times as great.

Both of these energies are extremely minute, but myriads of molecules add their energy to the field each second. And in comparison with the maser, the laser gives a very great deal more energy from each transition between energy levels. It should be easy to make a laser work, and this has turned out to be so. Further, the separation of the energy levels involved in the operation of a laser is large compared with thermal energies at room temperature. Boltzmann's distribution curve tells us that thermal energy will put a very small fraction of the atoms, molecules or ions used in a laser in *any* of the energy levels important to the operation of the laser. As a consequence lasers do not have to be cooled in order to operate, as three-level solid-state masers do. Some lasers do have to be cooled, however. Lifetimes of states often depend critically on temperature, and some lasers must be cooled for this reason. Also, some lasers must be cooled in order to keep them from burning up during continuous operation.

Another consequence of the comparatively large energy of a quantum in a laser is that the noise temperature of a laser amplifier is necessarily high. In Chapter III we saw that the noise temperature of an ideal amplifier is

$$T_n = \frac{hf}{k \ln 2} = 6.85 \times 10^{-11} f$$

From Table I we see that even the reddest light has a frequency of around 4.2×10^{14} cycles per second. Thus, an ideal linear amplifier for this light would have a noise temperature of 28,800°K. Actual laser amplifiers have been built with noise temperatures from two to three times this great. Clearly, quantum phenomena will add noise in amplifying signals that is much greater than that due to the electromagnetic radiation received from objects at room temperature.

As in the case of the maser, the operation of the laser depends on transitions between various energy levels, but the operation differs in some details. Lasers make use both of ions in crystals (the chromium ions in ruby, for instance) and atoms or molecules or ions of gas, such as neon. Pumping is accomplished by means of light in the ruby laser, and by means of a direct current or a radio frequency gas discharge in gaseous lasers. In the latter collisions of electrons with atoms or molecules or ions supply the pumping energy.

Figure 13 shows an energy-level diagram for a

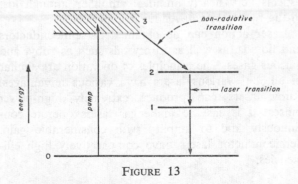

FIGURE 13

laser. The pumping action raises ions or atoms from the lowest level or *ground state* 0 to a group of energy levels 3. By means of nonradiative loss of energy (kinetic energy of collisions or vibration) the ions or atoms fall to the level 2. They then fall to the level 1 by adding energy to the electromagnetic field in the laser resonator.

For this transition the population of level 2 must be greater than that of level 1. The population of level 2 can be greater than that of level 1 even if thermal energies are sufficient to cause transitions from level 0 to level 1. However, in a device called the four-level laser the energy difference between levels 1 and 0 may be many times the thermal energy kT. When the energy difference between levels 1 and 0 is great, thermal energy will cause very few transitions from level 0 to level 1. If, further, the rate of spontaneous transitions between level 1 and level 0 is high, level 1 will be very nearly empty compared with level 2. When the population of level 1 is very small compared with the population of level 2, the laser is in its quantum mechanical aspects very nearly an ideal amplifier, though loss in the resonator can render it imperfect.

Laser action can be obtained in semiconductors and liquids, as well as in crystals such as ruby, and various gases. The principles of operation are similar in all, but various lasers have various advantages. Ruby lasers can produce extremely high-power pulses. It is easy to make gas lasers operate continuously and to amplify with considerable gain. Semiconductor lasers have comparatively high efficiencies.

The Physical Structure of Lasers

Because the wavelength of light is so short, the physical structure of lasers is very different from that of masers. Particularly, the resonators of lasers are tens of thousands to hundreds of thousands of wavelengths long, while maser resonators or maser traveling-wave circuits are at the most a few wavelengths long. I have found fascinating the behavior of the extremely short electromagnetic waves of the light produced by lasers, both inside and outside of resonators, and I propose to say a good deal about this.

First of all, why must the resonators of lasers be made so very many wavelengths long? The answer is not just that it is hard to make smaller structures. If lasers and masers are to produce a single frequency they must make use of one resonant mode of a resonator. Oscillation or amplification is attained when many excited atoms or molecules or ions are stimulated by the electromagnetic energy in a single mode or field pattern to radiate their energy and add it coherently to the oscillation already present.

The lowest frequency mode of oscillation in a resonator has a wavelength comparable to the length or breadth or circumference of the resonator. In a microwave maser a metallic enclosure or cavity of reasonable size can have as its lowest frequency the desired frequency of operation. Further, the electrical losses in the metallic walls of such a small cavity are low enough to allow efficient operation.

The wavelength of light is minuscule. If laser resonators are to be large enough to hold reasonable amounts of active material they must be a great many wavelengths long or broad. And there is another reason why laser resonators must be very large compared with a wavelength of light. In considering the loss of power in a microwave resonator we can talk in terms of the electrical resistance of the walls. This resistance increases as the frequency is increased, and hence the loss of power in the walls is greater at higher frequencies. We can also think of the loss of power in somewhat different terms. A metallic enclosure acts as a resonator because the electrically conducting walls reflect any microwaves which strike them, and so give rise to a standing wave rather than a traveling wave. The fraction of the electromagnetic power that a metallic surface reflects is dependent on the electrical resistance of the metal surface. This resistance increases with frequency. Thus, a shiny metal surface reflects a smaller fraction of light than it does of microwaves.

One way of reducing loss in a resonator is to put the reflecting walls of the resonator many wavelengths apart. Then the electromagnetic radiation travels without loss through the interior of the resonator a distance of many wavelengths between reflections. Reflections occur less frequently than in a small resonator, and, though the fraction of the power lost in each reflection is the same, the rate of power loss is lower.

This is the situation in resonators for lasers; they are made very large compared with a wavelength of light. But a resonator that is very large compared with the wavelength has many different modes or patterns of oscillation differing by only a small fraction in frequency and wavelength. Thus, while maser resonators have only one or a few modes of oscillation near the frequency of operation, laser resonators have many modes of oscillation near the frequency of oscillation, and it is sometimes difficult to get a laser oscillator to operate in just one mode at one frequency rather than to oscillate in several modes at several frequencies.

The rapidity of its development has been part of the fascination of the laser. The feasibility of maser action at optical and near optical frequencies was raised in 1958, in a paper published by Townes (of maser fame) and A. L. Schawlow. In 1960, less than two years later, T. H. Maiman succeeded in operating a pulsed ruby laser. He used a synthetic ruby crystal about a centimeter on a side, silvered on two opposing faces. When the crystal was exposed to a flash lamp, the yellow-green (5.5×10^{-5} cm wavelength) light supplied pumping power to invert the populations of a pair of energy levels, and the crystal produced a pulse of radiation with a wavelength of 6.93×10^{-5} cm, a deep red just within the range of visible light. Some subsequent ruby lasers have had narrow rods, around 0.1 cm in diameter and 2 or 3 cm long, for resonators. Of the polished, parallel ends, one is heavily metalized, and the other has a partially reflecting metallic coating which allows some of the light generated within the crystal to escape in a beam. The nature of the electromagnetic resonance in the ruby rod is such that the wave is successively reflected from the ends of the rod. Will the wave not escape from the side walls of the rod? These walls can reflect light, and so confine it to the interior of the rod, but this confinement is not necessary for the operation of a laser.

Imagine an infinite, plane electromagnetic wave, with every point on the wavefront traveling in the same direction. Imagine that a round mirror of diameter D is so placed that the wave strikes it perpendicularly. This apparatus is illustrated in Fig. 14. A beam of radiation will be reflected backward from the mirror. Initially the beam will have a diameter D and at first will maintain the diameter, the edges getting a little fuzzy. Eventually the reflected beam

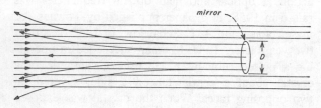

FIGURE 14

will diverge considerably in traveling away from the mirror, as I have tried to illustrate in a somewhat exaggerated manner in the figure.

We can put the matter quantitatively. The beam reflected by the mirror is parallel initially and sharp-edged. Very far from the mirror the beam is strongest near the axis and less intense away from the axis. But very far from the mirror all parts of the beam appear to diverge from a point. That is, very far from the mirror the reflected light travels along lines drawn from a single point. Further, a fair fraction of the energy lies within a cone of peak angle θ, where θ is given by

$$\theta = \frac{\lambda}{D} \text{ radians} = 57 \frac{\lambda}{D} \text{ degrees}$$

Here λ is the wavelength of the radiation. We see that the shorter the wavelength or the larger the mirror, the narrower the beam of radiation will ultimately be.

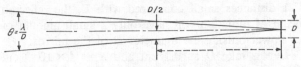

FIGURE 15

In Fig. 15 I have shown the mirror of diameter D, together with two lines perpendicular to its edges which represent the initial boundary of the reflected beam, and two lines diverging from its center at angles of $\theta/2$, which represent the boundaries of a cone containing a substantial fraction of the reflected light far from the mirror.

At some distance L from the mirror the parallel lines cross the diverging lines. It is reasonable to assume (and it turns out to be so) that at distances from the mirror which are small compared with L, the reflected beam is nearly parallel and has quite sharp edges. How long is L?

From the geometry of the figure

$$(D/2) = L \tan (\theta/2)$$

Ordinarily, θ is a very small angle, and so closely enough

$$\tan (\theta/2) = \theta/2$$

Hence, closely enough

$$D = L\theta$$

If we combine this with the earlier relation between θ, λ and D, we obtain

$$D = \frac{L\lambda}{D}$$

or

$$L = \frac{D^2}{\lambda}$$

For distances small compared with L, the reflected beam of radiation will have only a small amount of its power outside the diameter D of the mirror.

Let us take D as 0.1 cm and λ as 4×10^{-5} cm (the wavelength *in ruby* of the radiation produced by the ruby laser). We find that

$$L = 250 \ cm$$

Hence, of the radiation reflected at the ends of the ruby rod, only a little will spread out beyond the diameter in traveling the length of the rod.

Gas as a Laser Material

Sometimes a gas is used as a laser material. In this case (and the principle can be applied to solids) the mirrors may be put outside the tube containing the gas. Figure 16 shows a typical gas laser. The gas

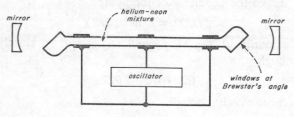

FIGURE 16

is confined within a glass envelope. The light passes in and out through carefully polished glass windows, which are at a particular angle with respect to the axis of the glass tube. The choice of this angle goes back to the work of Sir David Brewster, a Scottish physicist. Brewster discovered, in 1815, that light reflected from a glass surface at a particular angle of incidence, which depends on the refractive index of the glass, is completely polarized. The laws of electricity and magnetism (Maxwell's equations) explain this. We will not discuss the details but only the result.

Light is an electromagnetic wave. It has an electric field and a magnetic field perpendicular to each other, and both perpendicular to the direction in which the light travels, the direction of propagation. In ordinary, incoherent light the electric field points first in one direction and then in another. Or we can describe incoherent light as being made up of two parts or components whose electric fields are in two specified mutually perpendicular directions—horizontal and vertical, for instance. Polarized light is light whose electric field is always in one direction.[1] The direction of polarization is the direction of the electric field. Incoherent light is ordinarily unpolarized, but we can consider it to be made up of two polarized components.

Let us consider Fig. 16. If light whose electric field is parallel to the plane of the paper strikes the glass window at Brewster's angle, none is reflected. Thus, Brewster's angle is chosen to minimize light loss through reflection. Any light whose electric field is perpendicular to the plane of the paper in Fig. 16 is partially reflected, so only such light is reflected at all. In Brewster's experiment, the part of the incoherent light whose electric field was parallel to the glass was not reflected at all, and hence the reflected light had an electric field in the other specified direction only and, hence, was polarized.

By setting the windows of the laser of Fig. 16 at

[1] As, up *or* down; left *or* right.

Brewster's angle one can obtain negligible reflection for a wave of one polarization and appreciable reflection for a wave of the other polarization. The laser will tend to produce polarized light with the electric vector in the plane of the paper. If opposed plane mirrors are used to form a resonator for a laser, some of the radiation reflected from one mirror will miss the other. The electromagnetic field between the mirrors will become strongest at the center of the mirror and weaker near the edge. If D^2/λ is large compared with the separation of the mirrors, the loss of energy at the edges of the mirrors will be very small. This loss of energy can largely be eliminated by making either or both of the mirrors slightly concave. And this brings us to the complicated story of the electromagnetic resonator formed by two opposed concave mirrors. The understanding of this phenomenon is a triumph of the practical application of Maxwell's equations.

The Application of Maxwell's Equations to Coherent Light

We find that there are solutions to Maxwell's equations (that is, possible electromagnetic waves) that can exist between such concave mirrors.[2] If we consider the field strength as a function of distance from the axis (the line passing through the centers of curvature of the two mirrors) we find that several different patterns or modes are possible. To describe these we must refer to a set of directions or co-

[2] This is true only if the mirrors are closer together than the sum of their radii of curvature.

ordinates. The ones we will use are shown in Fig. 17.

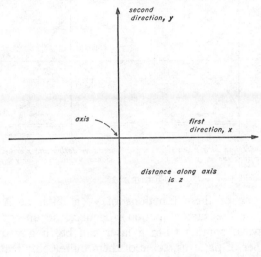

FIGURE 17

Here we are looking along the axis of the tube. Distance to the right of the axis (in the x-direction) is called x and distance above the axis (in the y-direction) is called y. Distance along the axis (in the z-direction) is called z.

Suppose we consider the strength of the field as a function of distance from the axis in the x-direction, and also as a function of distance from the axis in the y-direction. We find that the field can vary in each direction in a number of ways. The two simplest are shown in Fig. 18. The others have more wiggles.

We find, in fact, that the way the field strength varies perpendicular to the axis can be expressed as a product of any one of these functions of x times

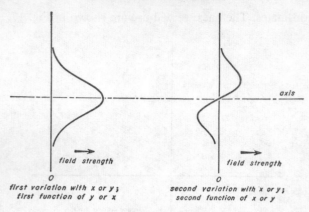

axis

field strength   field strength

first variation with x or y;   second variation with x or y;
first function of y or x   second function of x or y

FIGURE 18

any one of these functions of *y* (a different function, or the same function). Hence, the energy of the wave coming from a laser can be in any of a number of patterns, some of them quite complicated. A few of these are indicated in Fig. 19.

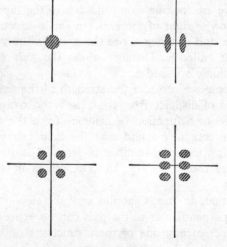

FIGURE 19

How does the electromagnetic field vary along the
beam between the mirrors? Midway between mirrors
the wave travels parallel to the axis. To the left and
right it diverges, as shown in Fig. 20. Far enough
from the midpoint, the wave diverges from the midpoint on the axis. Mathematically, the wave travels
out along a family of hyperbolas asymptotic to lines
through the midpoint of the axis. Figure 20 shows
two of these hyperbolas.

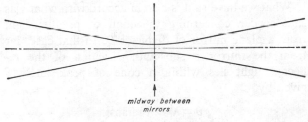

midway between
mirrors

FIGURE 20

Normal (that is, perpendicular) to the axis the
pattern of intensity is that discussed in connection
with Figs. 18 and 19. As we move along the axis
away from the midpoint, the pattern of intensity
grows in size but does not change in shape. The size
varies in proportion to the distance between the
hyperbolas of Fig. 20.

We have seen that as we move out along the axis,
far from the midpoint the hyperbolas approach their
asymptotes, which are straight lines going through
the midpoint, as shown in Fig. 20. Thus, far from
the midpoint the width of the pattern is proportional
to distance from the midpoint. Some substantial fraction of the energy of the beam of light will lie within
a cone of peak angle θ. This angle is proportional
to λ/D, where λ is the wavelength of the light and

D specifies the width of the beam of light at the midpoint, where the light travels parallel to the axis.

All the foregoing is in general accord with our idea of geometrical optics, that light travels in straight lines. Far from the midpoint, where the intensity pattern is large, the radiation does travel in straight lines. But near the midpoint, where the pattern is small, only the wave nature of light can account for the curved paths in which the radiation travels.

What we have said is also in accord with what was said earlier concerning reflection of parallel light from a plane mirror of diameter D. In that case, far from the mirror a substantial fraction of the reflected light lies within a cone of peak angle θ given by

$$\theta = \lambda/D \text{ radians}$$

Other Laser Phenomena: The Narrow Beam

Maxwell's equations—the laws of electricity and magnetism—account beautifully for the complicated behavior of the radiation trapped between the two mirrors of a laser, and predict exactly the various patterns that such radiation can have. They also account for many fascinating aspects of the behavior of the coherent light produced by lasers. One striking aspect is that light from lasers can be focused into unprecedentedly narrow beams. The width of a searchlight beam is fixed rather by the dimensions of the light source than by the wave nature of light. To increase the amount of radiation we can increase the temperature of the source, or the area of the source. The melting point and evaporation of refractory materials limit the temperature we can attain to about 2800°K in an incandescent lamp and 4000°K in an arc lamp. If we use the highest permissible temperature, we can increase the amount of radiation only by increasing the area of the radiator, and this increases the width of the beam of radiation.

We can treat this matter quantitatively. Let p be the power per square meter of visible and invisible electromagnetic radiation emitted by an incandescent surface in directions lying within a cone of half peak angle θ. Then[3]

$$p = 5.73 \times 10^{-8} \, eT^4 \sin^2\theta$$

Here e is the emissivity of the surface (which cannot be greater than unity), T is the temperature of the surface in degrees Kelvin, and, as we have noted, a cone of half peak angle θ includes the directions of travel of the emitted power density p. By letting $\theta = \pi/2$ so that $\sin \theta = 1$ we obtain the total power density radiated from the surface.

It can be shown that no focusing system gives more power density than that expressed by this equation, where T is taken as the temperature of the radiation source. Hence, the most total power we can obtain from a disk source of diameter D (the lens or mirror of a searchlight, for instance) can be expressed by means of this equation, using $e = 1$. This power P is

$$P = (\pi/4)D^2p = 4.50 \times 10^{-8}T^4D^2\sin^2\theta$$

Thus, for a total power P, diameter D and temperature T the least half-angle of the cone of radiation will be given by

[3] The Appendix may help the reader here.

$$\sin \theta = \sqrt{\frac{P}{4.50 \times 10^{-8} T^4 D^2}}$$

If θ is small, the sine of θ can be taken as equal to the angle measured in radians, and we can write

$$\theta = \frac{4720 \sqrt{P}}{DT^2} \text{ radians}$$

The radiation from an incandescent surface comes from many modes of oscillation of different frequencies, whose intensities are determined by thermal energy. A laser beam comes from one mode of oscillation, of a constant frequency and an intensity determined by the nature of the laser material and the degree or intensity of pumping.

Whatever the power of a laser beam, the half peak angle of the cone of radiation it produces is approximately

$$\theta = \lambda/2D \text{ radians}$$

Let us now make a comparison. Let the total power of thermal radiation be 1 watt, the diameter of the searchlight lens be 0.1 meter (10 cm), and the temperature be that of an arc, 4000°K. We find

$$\theta = 2.95 \times 10^{-3} \text{ radians}$$

Now let us make a calculation of the angular width of a laser beam. If we take the wavelength as 5×10^{-5} cm and the diameter of the lens as 10 cm, we find

$$\theta = 2.5 \times 10^{-6} \text{ radians}$$

The beam is scarcely a thousandth as wide as the beam from an ideal incandescent light source which we considered above.

The narrowness of the beam from a laser is truly striking, even when (because several modes of oscillation are present or because the focusing system is imperfect) the beam width is greater than what one calculates by the simple formula given. Thus, L. D. Smullin and G. Fiocco, in 1962, used a twelve-inch telescope to direct the light from a laser at the moon and managed to detect the reflected light using a forty-eight-inch telescope. The calculated width of the laser beam at the moon was about half a mile. The actual width was about fifty miles, but this is still a very narrow beam, only a fortieth the diameter of the moon.

Granularity

Another astonishing fact about the laser is the appearance of the bright spot produced when the beam of a laser strikes a diffuse reflecting surface such as a wall. The spot appears mottled or roughly dotted. The pattern of spots moves and changes as the observer moves his head.

Oddly enough, some physicists and engineers did not understand the reason for this phenomenon when they first noted it. I say oddly, because radio engineers are familiar with something exactly similar and particularly noticeable in mobile radio. As a car receiving an UHF radio signal moves among houses, the signal it receives fluctuates sharply with position. The explanation is that at some points the radio signals reflected from various houses add up in phase and at other points they cancel out.

Similarly, at some points on the retina of the eye the waves reflected from various high and low portions of the diffuse surface add up, and at other points on the retina of the eye various reflections arrive in opposite phases and cancel. This effect completely explains the dotted or mottled appearance which the eye (and also the film of a camera) observes. It can be shown that the grain size of the spottiness should depend on the size of the lens used to produce an image. A large lens should give a fine-grained dottiness, while a small lens should give a coarse dottiness. This is found to be so.

Why don't we commonly see this dotty pattern in a spot of ordinary light? We could state the explanation in several ways, but one will suffice. If we could look at the spot of ordinary light for the tiniest fraction of a second through a filter passing light of a very narrow range of frequencies only, we would see a dotty pattern. What the eye sees is the sum of many patterns of dottiness of different frequencies or colors of light, each pattern fluctuating exceedingly rapidly, and all patterns adding together. On the average, as the eye sees it, the result is an even, steady spot of light. The granularity can, however, be demonstrated under special experimental conditions using broadband light.

Holograms

The work of Emmet Leith and his associates at the University of Michigan with "holograms" is one of the most beautiful examples of the use of the coherent wave phenomena of laser light. It is easiest to explain this work by means of the concrete example illustrated in Fig. 21. The upper part of the figure illustrates the production of a hologram. A part of a coherent beam of light from a laser falls on a photographic plate, and another part of the beam is reflected by a mirror so as to fall on an object to be photographed (a flower pot in Fig. 21). In turn the light reflected by the object to be photographed falls on the photographic plate. At a par-

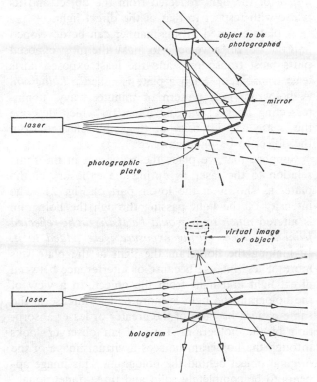

FIGURE 21

ticular point on the plate, the light reflected from the object can arrive in phase or out of phase with the direct light from the laser. When the direct light and the reflected light arrive in phase the total light is more intense than the direct light alone; when the reflected light arrives out of phase with the direct light the total light is less intense than the direct light alone. Thus, the total exposure of the photographic plate at a point depends on both the *magnitude* of the light reflected from the object and its *phase* with respect to that of the direct light.

A plate exposed in this manner can be developed and the image "reversed" to make the most exposed parts most transparent and the least exposed parts least transparent. Such a plate is called a *hologram*. A hologram is a pattern of minute, wavy, nonintersecting lines of varying intensity, which describe the phase and intensity of the light reflected from the object to be photographed.

Suppose that we place the hologram in the same relation to the laser as during the exposure of the plate, as shown in the lower part of Fig. 21. The intensity of the light passing through the hologram is altered *much as it would be if the light reflected from the object during exposure were added to it.* In making the hologram the light at the plate was more or less intense because of interference between direct light and light from the object. In a view of the hologram the light is more or less intense in the same pattern because of the greater or lesser absorption of the hologram. Thus, if an observer looks through the hologram he sees a virtual image of the original object behind the hologram. This image appears to be completely solid and three-dimensional.[4]

In all, the laser has truly opened our eyes to the

[4] The reversal of the plate, black into clear and clear into black, is not necessary; the difference between a "positive" and a "negative" hologram merely produces a difference in phase of the light forming the image, and the eye is insensitive to phase. The reversal of the plate was put in to make the explanation simpler.

unique fascinations of coherent light. It will un-
doubtedly lead to new and useful achievements in
communication and other fields, but these lie largely
in the future. The laser is so fresh, so novel, so unprecedented that it is hard to fit it into our technical
world.

Chapter V

SEMICONDUCTOR DEVICES

This book opened with a panegyric to the transistor, but we have been a good many pages getting to an explanation of this revolutionary device. The transistor is still sealed in a metal can the size of a pencil eraser, hidden from the eye and inscrutable to the mind of the reader. It is not that we have been saving the best for the last, although the practical importance of the transistor far outweighs that of the maser or laser. Transistors (mainly to our benefit but too often to our annoyance) are all about us. The 100,000 transistors in a large electronic computer enable it to carry out operations that would have been impractical with vacuum tubes. Transistors have increased the performance of long-distance telephone transmission, and they soon will give us undersea telephone cables with several times the capacity of existing cables, which use vacuum-tube amplifiers. Transistors are an indispensable part of communication satellites such as TELSTAR, Relay, and Syncom, and of other types of satellites as well. Transistors made possible the ubiquitous pocket radio, whose jangle was faintly echoed in the second paragraph of the first chapter of this book.

The real reason for putting the transistor last is to make it easier to explain. In masers and lasers we deal with atoms, or ions, or molecules individually, and when we consider their interaction with their environment or with an electromagnetic field, we can consider each atom, ion, or molecule independently. The crystalline semiconductor material of which a transistor is formed, however, is made up of a host of atoms arranged in a regular pattern, and its properties can be explained only by considering the behavior of such a regular array of atoms. In understanding this, we will use what we have already learned about quantum phenomena, but we will have to add new things as well.

How old are the new things we must know in order to understand the transistor? Some of them were not apparent before the discovery of the transistor effect, in 1948, a discovery for which W. H. Brattain, John Bardeen and W. B. Shockley received the Nobel Prize in 1956. But others were understood much earlier. Leafing through a book rather recently, I found a typewritten memorandum headed, "MOTT AND JONES SEMINAR DECEMBER 8, 1938." Shockley was then leading a seminar based on *Properties of Metals and Alloys,* by N. F. Mott and H. Jones, a book published in 1936. The volume contains most of the quantum ideas one needs to understand the transistor, and those ideas had been gathered largely from then-recently published work. So there exists a body of theory, at least, that goes back more than twenty-five years.

Both ideas and "things" were necessary for invention of the transistor. Theoretical understanding of the behavior of semiconductors was needed, and only quantum mechanics could provide this. A second essential was extremely pure semiconducting material, in which free negative electrons and positive charges[1] could coexist together for appreciable lengths of time. The radar receivers of World War II used silicon or germanium "crystal detectors," and during and after the war methods were worked out for producing extremely pure silicon and germanium. In impure semiconductors unlike charges quickly recombine. A pre-transistor physicist would have regarded a device whose operation depended on the simultaneous presence of charges of unlike signs as extremely improbable. The third requirement for invention of the transistor was the application of able and inquiring minds to grapple with the dual problem of making a new type of amplifier and understanding the puzzling and peculiar phenomena encountered.

At the beginning of the search, the investigators were armed with the new understanding provided by quantum mechanics, with materials of unprecedented purity and with one idea of how an amplifier might be made.[2] During the search, the investigators encountered and then understood the transistor effect, and so invented an amplifier quite different in principle from that which they were seeking. It would be pointless to try to describe all the steps through which understanding was attained. Rather, we will try to share the understanding itself.

Atomic Structure and Energy Levels

In making or studying the transistor we must concern ourselves with the motions of electrons through

[1] The explanation of these positive charges as something aptly called *holes* is given later in this chapter.
[2] This sort of amplifier was finally realized as the *field effect transistor*.

the regular array of atoms that constitutes a crystal-line material. If we are to understand the motion of electrons through a crystal, we must go back to an idea with which we have already become familiar, the concept of energy levels.

Until now, we have thought of energy levels as pertaining to the atom as a whole. We have said that an atom can be in the ground state, or in various excited states, which have more energy, and we have said that an atom can pass from one state to another with the absorption or emission of energy. We have not asked what the physical difference is between an atom in an excited state and an atom in the ground state.

An atom consists of a positive core or nucleus and a number of electrons traveling around the nucleus according to the laws of quantum mechanics. The equations the electrons obey are wave equations, and so the behavior of the electrons has something in common with the behavior of the photons of light.

When an atom is in the ground state, electrons move about the nucelus in such a way that the atom as a whole has the least possible energy allowed by the laws of quantum mechanics. For many (but not all) atoms, this restriction means that all the electrons are as close to the nucleus as the laws of quantum mechanics allow them to be. One common and simple excited state of an atom is that in which the outermost electron (or one of the outermost electrons) is moved farther away from the nucleus.

According to the laws of quantum mechanics, the outermost electron can have only particular motions about the nucleus, at particular distances, and these motions are described by particular wave patterns or *wave functions,* which we can liken to the various modes of an electromagnetic resonator. Referring to Fig. 7, we would say that the energy of the outermost electron when it was as close as allowed to the nucleus would represent the ground state E_0 of the atom. The next outward allowable pattern of motion would correspond to the energy E_1, the next to E_2, etc.

In this particular case of an atom with an outermost electron at various distances we have a simple physical explanation or description of the various states or energy levels of the atom. These states correspond to different energies of the outermost electron as it moves in a pattern which is closer to or farther away from the nucleus. Hence, in this particular case, we can think of the different energies as pertaining to the outermost electron, rather than to the atom as a whole.

We are now going to ask what happens to the motions of electrons and the wave patterns or wave functions which describe these motions when we put atoms close together, as they are in a crystal. But before we proceed, we should recall something from Chapter I.

Both electrons and photons, we emphasized, have wave properties. The various resonances of the electromagnetic resonator, each with its characteristic energy hf, correspond to different wave patterns, each with its characteristic energy. And we can put as many photons as we wish in any one wave pattern —that is, in fact, how we get coherent light in a laser. The different energy levels of an excited atom correspond to different wave patterns, or wave functions, which describe the motion of the outermost electron. As we noted in Chapter I, we *cannot* put many electrons in one wave pattern. Electrons differ in a quantity called *spin*. Two electrons of opposite spin can have one wave pattern. A law, called Pauli's *exclusion principle,* states that two electrons with opposite spins are the greatest number that can share one wave pattern or wave function.[3]

Electron Motion in a Crystal

Suppose that two atoms are initially far apart, so far apart that neither has any appreciable effect on the other. Then the outermost electron of each can be in any one of a sequence of energy levels, which will be the same for each atom and each electron. But suppose now that we move the atoms close enough together so that the nucleus of one exerts forces on the electrons of the other. What happens? All the energy levels characteristic of the individual atom are split into pairs of energy levels, as illustrated in Fig. 22. Each energy level now corresponds

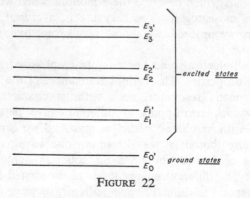

FIGURE 22

[3] Alternatively, we can say that wave patterns come in pairs whose energies differ very slightly, one corresponding to one electron spin and the other to the other electron spin. In this sense there can be only *one* electron per wave pattern.

to a wave function or pattern of motion involving *both* atoms. The two closely spaced energy levels of a pair correspond to different wave functions or patterns of motion.

Figure 23 illustrates qualitatively (above) a par-

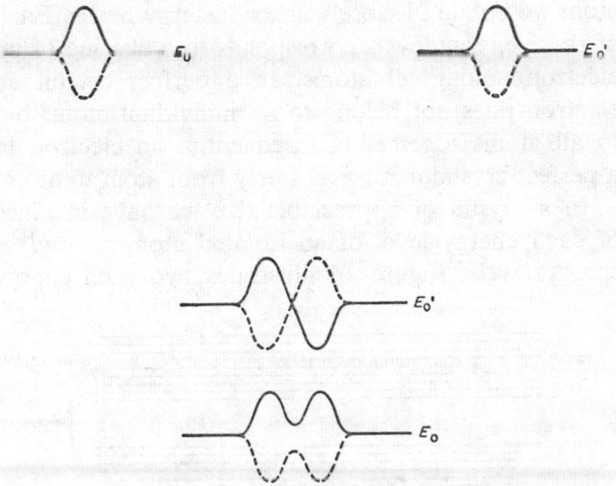

FIGURE 23

ticular wave function of two widely separated atoms and (below) the two different wave functions of the atoms when they are brought close enough together so that both nuclei affect the motions of the electrons. These two wave functions are distortions of the upper wave functions, joined together in different ways.

We should note particularly the following: When we move two atoms close together, we don't change the total number of electrons, and we don't change the total number of wave functions or energy levels. We obtain two closely spaced levels, corresponding to each energy level of an individual atom, and each of these corresponds to a sharing of an electron by both atoms.

What happens when we put a large number N of atoms together, regularly spaced in a crystalline structure? For each energy level of an individual atom we obtain N closely spaced energy levels. Each of these energy levels corresponds to a sharing of an electron among all atoms. In a perfect crystal an electron does not belong to an individual atom, but to all atoms together. Consequently, an electron in a perfect crystal can travel freely from atom to atom.

In a crystal of appreciable size we have in place of each energy level of an isolated atom a *band* of energy levels. Figure 24 illustrates two such energy

FIGURE 24

bands. If an electron has an energy lying in one of these energy bands it can move freely through the crystal; otherwise it cannot.

Because energy corresponds to frequency ($E = hf$), we can say also that electrons having certain ranges of frequencies can pass through the crystal. Thus, a crystal stands to electrons as an electric filter that passes a certain band of frequencies stands to electromagnetic waves or photons.

We can talk about the electrons in a crystal in terms of either standing waves or traveling waves.

The two approaches are equivalent, for two traveling waves moving in opposite directions produce a standing wave. In terms of traveling waves the travel can be in various directions. Let us consider motion in two opposite directions, left and right. An energy band in a crystal will be made up of a large number of waves of different energies representing motion to the left and an equal number of waves with the same energies representing motion to the right. Thus, each energy level corresponds to two waves, one traveling to the left and the other to the right.

Now there is a relation between the number of waves and the number of electrons, for both numbers are proportional to the number of atoms. This relation is vitally important to the electrical behavior of the crystal. Any particular wave function or energy level can be occupied by two electrons having opposite spins. Thus, for each energy level we can have two electrons (of opposite spins) traveling to the left and two electrons (of opposite spins) traveling to the right, and no more. Each energy level is thus a sort of two-way street by means of which an electron can travel with a particular energy and speed either to the right or to the left. For a given energy level two electrons, of opposite spins, are allowed in each direction, and no more.

Conductors, Insulators and Semiconductors

Some crystals are insulators or nonconductors of electricity. Absolutely pure silicon and germanium held at a very low temperature are quite good insulators. How can this be? In insulators the energy bands lying above a certain energy are completely empty, as in Fig. 25. Obviously, no electric current can flow as the result of an empty energy band. It turns out to be equally true that no current can flow as the result of a completely filled energy band. In a completely filled energy band there is an electron

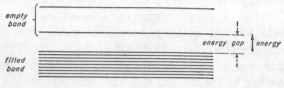

FIGURE 25

going to the right for every electron going to the left. Every energy level is a two-way street for no more than two pairs of electrons at a time, and every energy level is occupied by two pairs of electrons, one pair going each way. If a very strong electric field were applied to the material, an electron might jump from the highest filled band to the lowest empty band and so become free to move, but an extremely large electric field would be needed.

In conductors such as pure metals a particular *conduction band* is only partly filled with electrons. When an electric field is applied some electrons going one way can transfer to slightly higher empty energy levels and travel in the other direction. Since a few more electrons will be traveling in one direction than in the other, an electric field can make a net electric current flow.

Metals are good conductors. Some substances obdurately remain insulators. A third class of materials, called semiconductors, can conduct electricity when they contain certain impurities in very minute quantities. Silicon and germanium are semiconductors.

The presence of impurities in silicon or germanium can act in one of two ways. The presence of small amounts of one group of elements, including phosphorus, antimony, and arsenic, adds electrons to the empty levels. When there is no electric field applied, these electrons settle down four to a level, two traveling to the right and two to the left. But if a small electric field is applied so as to force electrons toward the right, some electrons which initially were traveling to the left jump into vacant levels of a shade higher energy and travel to the right. An electric field applied so as to urge electrons toward the left similarly will cause electrons to jump to levels in which they can move toward the left.

Another group of substances, including boron, aluminum, and gallium, make silicon or germanium conducting; they take away electrons from a filled energy band, leaving the band in a not filled but "almost filled" condition. As before, in the absence of an electric field there is an electron traveling to the right for each electron traveling to the left. When an electric field is applied, some electrons traveling against the electric field will jump to one of the few vacant levels and travel in the direction in which the electric field urges them to go.

If we could see the motion of electrons in this case of the almost filled energy band, we would see among the filled levels a few vacancies or holes where electrons, if they were present, could be traveling to the right or left. When the mathematics of the almost filled energy band is worked out, it shows a behavior exactly like that we would expect from positive charges traveling through the crystal. Experiment confirms this perhaps astonishing mathematical picture. The physical behavior is like that we ordinarily associate with the motion of positive charges. Thus, there is a real reason to think of the conduction as due to *holes* in the almost filled band, holes that act as free positive charges would act.

Materials such as phosphorus, antimony, or arsenic, which, when present in germanium or silicon, add electrons to an empty band, are called n-type impurities or *donors* because of the negative electrons they add. Silicon or germanium containing n-type impurities is called n-type silicon or germanium.

Materials such as boron, aluminum, or gallium, which, when present in germanium or silicon, remove electrons from filled bands and create holes that behave like positive charges and are free to move, are called p-type impurities, or *acceptors*. Germanium or silicon containing p-type impurities is called p-type germanium or silicon.

Either n-type or p-type impurities are sometimes called *doping agents,* and their addition to a crystal is called doping. The more of an n- or a p-type impurity there is in a semiconductor the better it will conduct electricity. Adding a p-type or n-type impurity increases the conductivity or (the same thing) decreases the resistivity of a semiconductor.

Electrons do not flow freely in semiconductors with large admixtures of impurities; they go a short distance and then bump into an irregularity in the crystal structure and change course. To attain anything approximating the free motion one would have in a perfectly pure and regular crystal, one must use a very pure semiconductor. Very pure semiconductors and very perfect single crystals are absolutely essential for good transistors.

There are a number of ways of purifying silicon

and germanium. Very perfect single crystals can be made by touching a seed crystal to the surface of silicon or germanium that is just at the melting point. When the seed crystal then is pulled slowly upward, a crystalline rod emerges from the liquid. The semiconductor can be of either n-type or p-type; the crystal will almost always be purer than the melt.

The Semiconductor as Diode

Let us suppose that the material in the crucible will produce an n-type crystal because we have added enough n-type impurity for it to predominate. Suppose that a crystalline rod has been partly formed by pulling from the molten material. At this point we add enough p-type impurity to the molten material for it to predominate over the n-type impurity in the grown crystal. Then, as the rest of the crystal is formed, it will be p-type, not n-type. There will be a p-n junction between the two types of material. Such a junction acts as a rectifier. That is, current can flow across the p-n junction in one direction only.

The junction is illustrated at the left in Fig. 26.

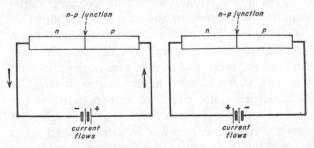

FIGURE 26

When the p-type material is connected to the positive pole of a battery and the n-type to the negative pole, an electric current can and does flow through the material and across the junction. The filled band of the p-type material has a few holes in it; these can flow into the corresponding completely filled band of the n-type material (really, electrons move from the completely filled band of the n-type material into the holes in the corresponding band of the p-type material). Electrons can flow from the almost empty band of the n-type material into the corresponding but completely empty band of the p-type material.

What happens if the negative pole of the battery is connected to the p-type material and the positive pole is connected to the n-type material, as in the right of Fig. 26? No current flows. The electric field is such as to urge holes from the filled band of the n-type material to the corresponding almost filled band of the p-type material, but there are no holes in the n-type material to move. The field is also such as to urge electrons to move from the empty band of the p-type material to the corresponding almost empty band in the n-type material, but there are no electrons in the empty band of the p-type material to move. No current, or almost no current, flows.

Germanium and silicon *diodes* consisting of p-n junctions are extremely valuable devices. They are used in computers, and as nonlinear devices for such functions as frequency changing in superheterodyne receivers. They are also used in parametric amplifiers, which we will discuss later. The solar cells that convert sunlight into power in satellites and other space vehicles consist of p-n junctions. But at this point, we will discuss another extremely valuable device incorporating two junctions.

The Semiconductor as Triode

Figure 27 shows the vital parts of a transistor. This

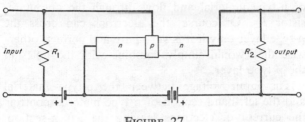

FIGURE 27

transistor consists of a section of n-type material, a very thin section of p-type material, and another section of n-type material, connected as shown. A battery makes the right-hand section of n-type material quite positive with respect to the p-type material. Thus, no current can flow from the p-type material, which acts as an input electrode, to the n-type material, which acts as an output electrode. Another battery makes the p-type material just a little positive with respect to the left-hand section of n-type material, so as to cause a flow of electrons from the n-type material into the p-type material, and a flow of a few holes from the p-type material to the n-type material as well. If there is more n-type impurity in the n-type material than there is p-type impurity in the p-type material, the current flow will be mainly electrons from the n-type to the p-type rather than holes from the p-type to the n-type.

What happens to these electrons entering the

p-type region from the n-type region? They might travel along the thin direction of the layer and into the input circuit, but the right-hand portion of n-type material is much closer, and it is positive and attracts them. Thus, almost all the electrons entering the p-layer from the left-hand section of n-type material go directly to the positive right-hand section of n-type material and flow through the output resistor R_2. Of course, the electrons can cross the p-type layer only if it is very pure and perfect; otherwise they would simply combine with the holes in the p-type layer.

The input voltage between the p-type material and the left-hand section of n-type material controls the current of electrons leaving the left n-section, but it is the right n-section that collects these electrons. The n-p-n transistor acts much like a triode vacuum tube. The left n-section corresponds to the cathode, which emits electrons, and is called the *emitter;* the p-layer, which is called the *base,* acts like the control grid, and the right n-section acts like the anode and is called the *collector.* In the triode the electrons leaving the hot cathode all pass the negative grid and reach the positive anode. In the good n-p-n transistor, almost all the electrons leaving the n-layer pass through the p-layer and reach the collector. But the current of electrons leaving the emitter is controlled much more strongly by the voltage of the p-layer than it is by the voltage of the collector, and so the n-p-n transistor is a very effective amplifier.

One can also make p-n-p transistors, in which a thin n-layer sandwiched between two p-layers controls a current of holes from the p-type emitter. In this case the collector must be held negative in order to collect holes rather than electrons. Such a transistor is illustrated in Fig. 28.

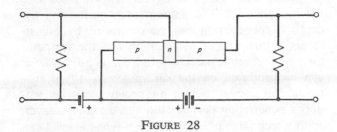

FIGURE 28

The operation of the transistor depends on a new principle—the simultaneous existence and the utilization of both negative electrons and positive holes in the same material (the base of the transistor). The success of the transistor depends on the purity of the materials used and on the ingenuity of the technique of fabrication.

The Diffused-Junction Mesa Transistor

Some transistors have the structure so far described. Others are made rather differently and have a different configuration, though the principle of operation is the same. A transistor called an *epitaxial double-diffused mesa* transistor can operate at frequencies well above a thousand megacycles because of its small size, the very thin layer of material between junctions, and proper conductivity of various regions.

We have seen how p-n junctions can be formed by adding a p-type impurity to n-type molten material containing an n-type impurity while a crystal is being pulled out of the molten material. Another way of producing a junction is to evaporate an impurity element onto a polished surface of hot silicon or germanium. The desired impurity diffuses into the hot material. The amount of impurity and the depth of penetration can be controlled by adjustments of the rate of evaporation and the temperature of the semiconductor. Indeed, a p-type layer can be produced on the surface of an n-type material, and then a thinner n-type layer can be produced penetrating partway through the p-type layer. With a technique of masking the n-type material can be diffused into a small area of the p-type layer.

Figure 29 shows the structure of a diffused-junc-

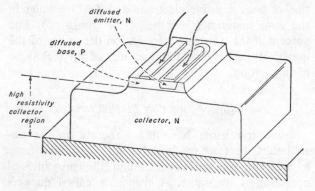

FIGURE 29

tion mesa transistor. For such a transistor, the starting material is a piece of relatively poorly conducting n-type silicon, in which the dominant electrical carriers are electrons. The surface of the silicon is highly polished and cleaned so that the subsequent diffusions will result in layers of uniform thickness. An element such as boron is first diffused into the whole silicon surface to a depth of about 0.15 thousandths of an inch to form a large area junction. Boron is a p-type impurity and acts as an acceptor of electrons. Other elements such as aluminum and gallium also may be used. Phosphorus, an n-type impurity or donor of electrons, is then diffused in many small areas into the boron layer to a depth of about 0.1 thousandth of an inch to form emitter regions. The p-type regions between junctions, 0.05 thousandth of an inch thick in each case, are the base regions. The resulting structures, after mesas have been etched to define the area of the collector junction at each emitter location, are n-p-n devices. To complete the fabrication, electrodes are attached to each of the three areas, the wafer is cut apart, and the transistors are sealed into cans with insulated lead-throughs.

The n-type collector region is made very much thicker than the emitter and base layers to provide both mechanical strength and ease of handling during fabrication. Since the region is made of relatively poorly conducting material, it also adds a high resistance in series with the collector, impairing operation at extremely high frequencies. The ideal solution to this problem is to form the main body of the collector from highly conducting material, leaving a thin layer of relatively poorly conducting material in the immediate vicinity of the collector junction. This can be done by starting with heavily doped material which has low electrical resistance but which, because of its impurities, cannot be used as the base of a transistor. Electrons in heavily doped p-type material cannot travel far enough before combining with a hole, and holes in heavily doped n-type material cannot travel far enough before combining with an electron. One then grows onto this impure material a very pure, high-resistance layer which continues the same regular crystal structure of the underlying material; this is called epitaxial growth. This pure epitaxial layer allows the electrons or holes to travel long enough distances to pass through the base region from the emitter junction to the collector junction. Such epitaxial growth can be obtained on silicon by exposing a heated silicon surface to a mixture of hydrogen and silicon tetrachloride vapor. Figure 30 shows an epitaxial transistor.

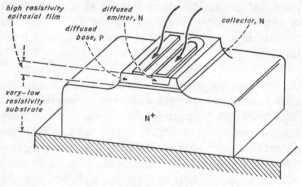

FIGURE 30

Other Semiconductor Devices

Although the transistor has had the most revolutionary effect of all semiconductor devices, other semiconductor devices are of great importance. Semiconductor diodes (illustrated in Fig. 26) have a widespread usage. Large silicon diodes, for example, are used in converting many kilowatts of alternating current power into direct current power for electroplating and other electrochemical processes. Smaller diodes are used in power supplies in radio and television sets, which also have diodes in the circuitry. Electronic computers and electronic switching systems incorporate hundreds of thousands of semiconductor diodes. Diodes are used as well in parametric amplifiers, which are important because they add very little noise to the amplified signal.

The Semiconductor as Capacitor

A circuit element called a *capacitor* consists of two closely spaced conducting electrodes separated by a dielectric. If a capacitor is connected to a battery, there will be an electric field in the dielectric, and there will be electric charges on the electrodes where the electric field terminates. Thus, a capacitor is capable of storing electric charge. The amount of charge stored is proportional to the voltage across the capacitor by a factor called the *capacitance* of the capacitor. If Q is electric charge stored in the capacitor, V the voltage across the capacitor and C the capacitance of the capacitor, then

$$Q = CV$$

The capacitance C of the capacitor is inversely proportional to the separation between the electrodes. Hence, the capacitance can be changed by changing this spacing. It can be shown that amplification can be obtained by means of a circuit including a capacitor if we can vary the capacitance of a capacitor at a frequency higher than the frequency of the signal to be amplified. This amplification involves transfer of energy to the signal to be amplified from whatever source of energy changes the capacitance of the capacitor. But, how can we change the capacitance of a capacitor fast enough?

Consider the junction diode with a battery connected across it, so that no current flows, as in the right of Fig. 26. To the left of the junction the semiconductor is conducting because it contains negative electrons that are free to move. To the right of the junction the semiconductor is conducting because it contains positive holes that are free to move. The battery produces an electric field across the junction and in the semiconductor near to the junction. The direction of this field is such as to drive free electrons away from the junction to the left, and free holes away from the junction to the right. Thus, the field produced by the battery drives all the electrons and holes, which could constitute an electric current, away from the vicinity of the junction, so that we have two conductors separated by a nonconducting region. The greater the battery voltage the thicker is the region from which holes and electrons are driven. Thus, increasing the battery voltage increases the thickness of the nonconducting dielectric region which separates the conducting n-type and p-type "electrodes." Hence, increasing the voltage decreases the capacitance of the diode.

We see that a p-n junction *biased* by a battery with such a polarity as to make it nonconducting acts as a capacitor, and the capacitance can be decreased by increasing the battery voltage. Semiconductor diodes are just the variable capacitors we need in order to make parametric amplifiers which will function even at microwave frequencies.

The Solar Cell

The *solar cell* is another important semiconductor diode. In order to understand its operation, we must consider what happens when the voltage of the battery connected to a p-n junction, as in Fig. 26, is neither positive nor negative, but zero—that is, when the battery is removed and a wire connects the two parts of the junction. We might think, mistakenly, that in this case there would be no electric field across the junction. Let us recall the conditions on each side of the junction. We will be concerned with two energy bands, as in Fig. 25. In the n-type semiconductor to the left of the junction, the upper "empty" band will not be quite empty; n-type impurities will have put a few conduction electrons in its lower energy levels. The lower filled band in the n-type semiconductor will be completely filled; there will be no holes in it. In the p-type semiconductor to the right of the junction, the upper empty band will be completely empty, but the p-type impurity will have produced a few holes in the upper energy levels of the lower "filled" band.

If there were no electric field across the junction, electrons would flow from the upper energy band of the n-type material into the upper empty band of the p-type material; this flow would constitute an electric current across the junction from the p-type material to the n-type material. Holes would flow from the lower band of the p-type material into the filled band of the n-type material; this flow would also constitute an electric current across the junction. The two electric currents flow in the same direction. Thus, if there were no electric field across the junction, we would have a steady flow of current through the junction and through the wire connecting the n-type material to the p-type material. We could use this current flow as a source of power. Clearly this is impossible; it would constitute perpetual motion.

We are forced to conclude that when the two sides of a p-n junction are connected together by a wire, there must be an electric field across the junction in a direction that prevents electrons from flowing from the n-type material into the p-type material, and prevents holes from flowing from the p-type material into the n-type material.

Now we will concern ourselves with another phenomenon. Consider again the filled and empty, or almost filled or empty, energy bands of Fig. 25. If somehow we could supply a considerable amount of energy to an electron in the filled band, we could move it up into the empty band. A photon of light of high enough frequency (and hence, of great enough energy) can do just this. When such a photon strikes a semiconductor, n-type or p-type, it produces a hole-electron pair: a positive hole in the lower band and a negative electron in the upper band.

Suppose we direct a beam of light at the p-n junction we have been considering, the n-type and p-type materials being interconnected by a wire. We have seen that there must be electric field across the junction. When a photon produces a hole-electron pair in or near the junction, the electric field immediately whisks the electron into the n-type material and the hole into the p-type material, and an electron flows in one direction and a hole in the other for each hole-electron pair produced. Thus, an electric current will flow from the n-type material to the p-type material as long as light falls on the junction. The light furnishes the power that we can derive from the electric current. A *solar cell,* which is merely a large p-n junction, can turn more than 10 per cent of the power of light falling on it into useful electric power. Solar cells supply the electric power needed in satellites such as TELSTAR, Relay, Syncom, and Tiros.

Solar cells are made from flat, highly polished sheets of silicon, of either n- or p-type. If this base material, for instance, is p-type silicon, it is heated and exposed to a vapor containing an n-type impurity, so as to form a p-n junction with a very, very thin layer of n-type material above it; this process produces an *n on p* solar cell. The n-type layer is made so thin as to be quite transparent to light. One electrical connection is made to the p-type base material; the other is made to the thin n-type layer, sometimes by means of "fingers" of thin conducting material which extend out over it. When light falls on the thin n-type layer, electric power can be obtained from the pair of terminals.

Limitations of Semiconductors

Semiconductor devices such as transistors, diodes, and solar cells are extremely useful, but they have limitations. One is the effect of temperature on their operation. At absolute zero temperature an electron will never jump from the filled band of a semiconductor to the empty band above, but as the temperature is raised, a few do, producing hole-electron pairs. Thus, even a perfectly pure semiconductor, without any impurities to supply electrons or holes, will become conducting if it is made hot enough. At such a temperature an n-type material will contain thermally produced holes as well as electrons, while a p-type material will contain thermally produced electrons as well as holes. When this happens in a diode or a transistor, the performance of the device is degraded.

How hot do we have to make a semiconductor in order to produce enough holes and electrons to seriously degrade its performance? It depends on the energy gap between the filled and the empty band. The wider this gap the more energy it takes to raise an electron from the filled band to the empty band, and the higher the temperature required to do so.

Germanium devices, with an energy gap of .67 volt, operate satisfactorily up to a temperature of 100°C, but their properties vary somewhat with varying temperature. The energy gap for silicon is 1.1 volts, and so silicon diodes and transistors are less affected by temperature than germanium devices, and can operate effectively at a temperature of 250°C. Gallium arsenide has a still larger energy gap, 1.4 volts, and gallium arsenide diodes remain good rectifiers at temperatures of 450°C.

The energy gap is only one of two highly important properties of a semiconductor; the other is the *mobility* of electrons or holes in the crystal. In a perfectly regular crystal an electron could travel freely forever, if its energy lay in an allowed band. In actual crystals an electron travels a short distance and is then deflected by some imperfection—either an impurity, or a distortion of the atomic spacing caused by the atomic vibrations constituting heat. The farther an electron or hole travels without being scattered the higher is the mobility. The electrical conductivity of a semiconductor is proportional to the mobility times the density of holes or electrons. The higher the mobility the better is the electrical performance of a diode.

Some materials, such as indium antimonide, have very high mobility. Excellent diodes for detectors and parametric amplifiers in the millimeter range of wavelengths (30,000 to 300,000 megacycles) have been made of indium antimonide.

The latest addition to the family of semiconductor devices is the semiconductor laser, or injection laser. In this device, the application of a sufficiently high voltage to a junction in the conducting direction raises electrons from the filled band to the empty band. The electrons eventually reach impurity levels just below the empty band and fall thence into the filled band, combining with holes and giving their energy to an electromagnetic field in the junction.

The Importance and Impact of the Semiconductor

The work of Brattain, Bardeen, and Shockley has had revolutionary effects in physics, in technology and in our everyday lives. Where would we be without transistor radios—or better, how can we get away from them? The invention of the transistor turned a whole generation of physicists to solid-state physics. This, in itself, assured further advances in the field.

The revolutionary importance of the transistor does not lie in a new mathematical formulation of nature's laws, such as Newton's laws of motion and gravitation, Maxwell's equations, Einstein's special theory of relativity, or Schroedinger's wave equation of quantum mechanics. The required theoretical groundwork was available in the book I studied with Shockley in 1938. The transistor effect, a manifestation of the simultaneous existence of negative electrons and positive holes in a semiconductor for a useful period of time, was a worthy outcome of ingenious experimentation and interpretation. But merely as physical phenomenon it would not have attracted the attention that it has received. It is primarily as an *invention* that the transistor is important. Here it ranks with the wheel, the steam engine, and the vacuum tube, that device which created an age of electronics, an age into which the transistor so aptly fits. Its technological power and sociological impact make the transistor overwhelmingly important.

Let no one say that the human individual cannot influence the course of the world. The sharp thought and painstaking work of Brattain, Bardeen and Shockley led to a new industry in Japan as well as in Europe and America. It led thousands of brilliant young physicists and engineers into the field of solid-state physics, which had been in the doldrums. The transistor brought the digital computer to a practical and useful form, and one could write many books about the wonders of computers, real and fictitious.

Individual thought is the most powerful social force in our world. But it is the solid fruits of thought, not our wailings into the wind, that change our world and our lives.

Appendix

MATHEMATICAL NOTATION

I have tried, whenever mathematics is necessary, to explain what I have said. Nonetheless, the notation is that of algebra, and this seems an appropriate place to say a few words about it to those who through years of disuse have forgotten some simple matters.

Letters are used to represent various quantities. I will illustrate this by the simple example of the area, A, of a rectangle of height h and width W.

We can say that the area, A, of a rectangle is the product of the height, h, and the width, W. This is the same as saying that A is h times W. Written out as an equation, the statement becomes:

$$A = hW$$

or

$$A = Wh$$

No multiplication sign is used. When one letter follows another, this means to multiply the two quantities.

If the rectangle is 2 feet wide and 4 feet high, we write:

$$A = (2)(4) = 8 \text{ square feet}$$

We use the parentheses as a sort of punctuation; we

cannot write 2 times 4 as 24—that means twenty-four.

Division is always written as a fraction. Thus, the statement that h is A divided by W is written:

$$h = \frac{A}{W} \quad \text{or} \quad A/W$$

We would read this, "h equals A over W."

If the rectangle is a square, and the length of each side is l, then

$$A = (l)(l) = l^2$$

The symbol l^2 (l squared) is simply the product, l and l.

The superscript 2 in l^2 is called an *exponent* and we say that in l^2, l is *raised to the second power*. We encounter other powers of various quantities in this book. For instance, just as

$$D^2 = (D)(D) \quad \text{or} \quad DD$$

so

$$T^4 = (T)(T)(T)(T) \quad \text{or} \quad TTTT$$

In the case of a square whose sides have a length l and whose area is A, we can write:

$$l = \sqrt{A}$$

This says that l is the square root of A. $\sqrt{A}$ multiplied by $\sqrt{A}$, that is, the square of the square root of A, is equal to A.

$$(\sqrt{A})(\sqrt{A}) = (\sqrt{A})^2 = A$$

In a numerical example,

$$(\sqrt{2})(\sqrt{2}) = (\sqrt{2})^2 = 2$$

The square root of 2 is approximately 1.414.

In using letters to represent quantities we sometimes use the same letter with subscripts to denote different quantities. Thus, different powers might be denoted as

$$P_0, \ P_1, \ P_n$$

and different resistors might have resistances

$$R_1, \ R_2$$

The strangest mathematical function I have used is the exponential function, which is written

$$e^x$$

Mathematically, this means the mathematical constant $e = 2.71828 \ldots$ (the dots represent an unending string of digits) raised to the x power. Practically, values of e^x are given for various values of x in Table A-I below.

Let us now as an example interpret an expression which appears in Chapter II

$$P_0 = G \left(\frac{hf}{e^{hf/kT} - 1} \right) B + (G - 1) B$$

Here the subscript 0 of P_0 designates a particular power, P_0, that we are talking about, the noise output power of the best possible linear amplifier. To evaluate $e^{hf/kT}$ we multiply Planck's constant h by the frequency f to get hf. We multiply Boltzmann's constant k by the absolute temperature T in degrees Kelvin to get kT. We divide hf by kT to get hf/kT. To find the value of $e^{hf/kT}$ we use Table A-I. To get $e^{hf/kT} - 1$ we subtract 1 from $e^{hf/kT}$. The quantity in the first parentheses on the right is then hf divided by the quantity $e^{hf/kT} - 1$. This quantity in the parentheses is to be multiplied by the power gain G and the bandwidth B in order to get the first term on the right, that is,

$$G\left(\frac{hf}{e^{hf/kT}-1}\right)B$$

To this we add the second term on the right

$$(G-1)B$$

To get this we subtract 1 from the power gain G and multiply the resulting quantity by the bandwidth B.

In Chapter IV, the function $\sin \theta$ is used. Here θ is an angle. Sin θ is a well-known trigonometric function related to a right triangle, shown in Fig. 31,

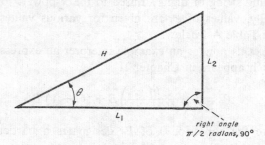

FIGURE 31

with sides of lengths L_1 and L_2 and a hypotenuse (the third side) of length H. Sin θ is defined as

$$\sin \theta = \frac{L_2}{H}$$

If we are to get numbers from the equations in the text, we need to know the values of various mathematical and physical constants. Some of these are given in the text, but I will summarize all here

$$\text{pi}, \pi = 3.1416 \ldots$$

natural logarithm of 2,

$$ln2 = .639 \ldots$$

Planck's constant,

$$h = 6.62 \times 10^{-34} \text{ joule seconds}$$

Boltzmann's constant,

$$k = 1.38 \times 10^{-23} \text{ joules/degree}$$

Physicists write large numbers in the following way:

$$10^9 \text{ (ten to the ninth)}$$
(that is, 1,000,000,000, or one billion)

$$10^{-4} \text{ (ten to the minus fourth)}$$
(that is, .0001 or one ten-thousandth)

In the upper example, the exponent 9 means that 10 has been multiplied by itself nine times.

$$10^9 = 10 \times 10 \times 10 \times 10 \times 10 \times 10 \times 10 \times 10 \times 10$$
$$= 1,000,000,000$$

We see that the exponent 9 is also the number of zeroes. In the case of the negative exponent, the meaning is

$$10^{-4} = \frac{1}{10 \times 10 \times 10 \times 10} = .0001$$

The negative exponent tells how many times we divide by 10.

A particular number will be written as follows, using the $\times$ sign for multiplication:

$$2.38 \times 10^5 \text{ (meaning 238,000)}$$
$$9.0 \times 10^{-2} \text{ (meaning .090)}$$

We write 9.0 to show that the quantity is accurate to two significant figures. That is, we guarantee only that the value is nearer to 9.0 than it is to 8.9 or to 9.1; it might be 8.98 or 9.04, for instance.

There is one more matter connected with the equations in the text. While I mention a variety of units, such as feet, pounds, and centimeters, the equations are all valid in the M.K.S. (meter-kilogram-second) system of units.

TABLE A-I

x	e^x
−5	.0067
−4	.018
−3	.050
−2	.14
−1	.37
− .5	.61
− .2	.82
− .1	.90
0	1
.1	1.1
.2	1.2
.5	1.6
1	2.7
2	7.4
3	20
4	55
5	150

INDEX

SCIENCE STUDY SERIES